NASA SP-423

Atlas of Mercury

Authors and Editors

Merton E. Davies, chief

The Rand Corporation

Stephen E. Dwornik

Lunar and Planetary Programs Office
Headquarters
National Aeronautics
and Space Administration

Donald E. Gault

Ames Research Center
National Aeronautics
and Space Administration

Robert G. Strom

Lunar and Planetary Laboratory
University of Arizona

Associates

JEANNE DUNN

Text Editor
The Rand Corporation

NANCY EVANS

Photographic Layout and Coordinator
Jet Propulsion Laboratory

JOEL MOSHER

Photographic Computer Processing
Jet Propulsion Laboratory

JURRIE VAN DER WOUDE

Photographic Preparation
Jet Propulsion Laboratory

ROBIN GREAVES

Graphic Design
Jet Propulsion Laboratory

NASA

National Aeronautics
and Space Administration

Scientific and Technical
Information Office

1978

Prepared for the Office
of Space Sciences,
National Aeronautics
and Space Administration

Dedication

This Atlas is dedicated to the members of the Television Science Team. It was their efforts, started almost five years before the spacecraft reached Mercury, that made this Atlas possible. Their technical and scientific capabilities, coupled with their dedicated motivation, produced the high quality photographs included in this book. The photographs will be used by scientists the world over to study and understand the processes that have shaped the surface of Mercury.

Bruce C. Murray, *Team Leader*
Michael J.S. Belton
G. Edward Danielson
Merton E. Davies
Donald E. Gault
Bruce W. Hapke
Gerard P. Kuiper
Brian O'Leary
Robert G. Strom
Verner R. Suomi
Newell J. Trask

Associates

James L. Anderson
Audouin Dollfus
John E. Guest
Robert J. Krauss

Foreword

The Mariner 10 mission to Venus and Mercury scored many firsts. It was the first multiple-planet mission, borrowing energy from the gravity of Venus to make possible a flight to Mercury otherwise unachievable. This required navigation of a precision never before attempted—equivalent to shooting a rifle bullet through a 2-inch knothole more than 100 miles away. During its Venus swingby, Mariner 10 took the first close-up photographs of Venus, revealing the intricate spiral structure in its cloud layers that confirmed the classic circulation theory hypothesized by the astronomer Hadley more than 200 years ago and believed to be the basic driving mechanism behind weather on Earth. On the way from Venus to Mercury, Mariner 10 also made the first practical use of solar sailing, a novel technique that I predict will be used increasingly in the future to replace more expensive space propulsion systems. And as it flew by Mercury, Mariner 10 entered an orbit that, for the first time, provided two subsequent flyby revisits.

The hard-working Mariner 10 team also scored a number of management firsts. It was the first space project team to ever receive a NASA performance award *prior to* launch—a tribute to their determination and skill in pioneering daring techniques to cut the cost of space missions at the same time they were actually upgrading the quality of the science return.

Of all the firsts, undoubtedly the outstanding achievement of the Mariner 10 mission was the spectacular unveiling of the planet Mercury. Mercury's closeness to the Sun makes it an almost impossible object for astronomical study, and the total knowledge of Mercury prior to Mariner 10 was miniscule. Even its rate of rotation was not determined until 1965. Mercury's surface was almost totally unknown, with considerable conjecture that total surface melting could have left Mercury as smooth as a billiard ball.

Then came the tiny Mariner 10 spacecraft, a bright sunlit speck of a solar sailing craft speeding in from the blackness of space. Aboard was an imaging system born of the ingenuity and close cooperation between space systems engineers and the scientists of the imaging experiment team. Using a narrow-angle television camera, it could take only postage-stamp-size pictures of the surface. But it could flash them back to Earth with such rapidity that it was possible to map the entire lighted portion of the planet with excellent resolution.

This Atlas is a tribute to the accomplishments of that highly productive team effort. As you turn its pages you will see the face of Mercury as it was unveiled to mankind for the very first time. If it is not a beautiful face, it is nevertheless a most fascinating one, marked with a character all its own, including "wrinkles" over 2000 km long. Even its noticeable similarities to the Moon are fascinating—why should both the Moon and Mercury have the smooth mare areas located predominantly on one face with rough highlands on the other? Why should Mercury, so far from the asteroid belt, have a surface just as pocked by bombardment as the Moon? Clearly, adding the portrait of Mercury to our gallery of terrestrial planets will contribute greatly to our knowledge of the violent accretion process that formed the planets.

Even with the two revisits of Mariner 10 to Mercury, we have seen only one side of the planet—a limitation imposed by Mercury's harmonic rotational lock to the Sun. I wait with eager anticipation for the day when we return to see the other face of Mercury.

Robert S. Kraemer
Director, Lunar and Planetary Programs
National Aeronautics and Space Administration
October 1976

Contents

The Planet

Introduction

The planet Mercury played an important role in the religious life of many ancient civilizations. Although Mercury was probably seen by prehistoric man, the first recorded observation was by Timocharis in 265 B.C. The early Greeks believed that the east and west elongations of Mercury represented two separate objects which they called Hermes (evening star) and Apollo (morning star). When later Greeks recognized that Mercury was one object, they designated it Hermes, the messenger of the gods and god of twilight and dawn who announced the rising of Zeus. The ancient Egyptians, however, first discovered that Mercury (called by them Sabkou) orbited the Sun. To the Teutonic peoples Mercury was known as Woden, and our anglicized version of the midweek day Wednesday is derived from the original Woden's Day. The present name Mercury is derived directly from the Latin name Mercurius, which is the Roman designation for the Greek name Hermes.[1,2]

The Italian astronomer Zupus first observed the phases of Mercury in 1639. They were later observed independently by Hevelius in 1644. The transit of the Sun by Mercury, first predicted by Kepler in 1630, was observed by Gassendi, and the first recorded observations of surface markings were by Schröter and Harding in 1800. In the same year, Schröter incorrectly measured a rotation period of 24 hours with a rotation axis inclined 70° to the orbital plane. Another incorrect rotation period of 88 days determined by Schiaparelli[1,2] 80 years later was not corrected until the advent of recent radar observations, which in turn were confirmed by measurements made by Mariner 10.[3,4]

MERCURY

Of all the planets in the solar system, Mercury is closest to the Sun (Figure 1). Because it is never more than 28 angular degrees from the Sun as viewed from the Earth, telescopic observations must be made during daytime or at twilight through a long path length of the Earth's atmosphere. As a consequence, telescopic observations are poor compared with those of most other planets.

Mercury is the smallest terrestrial planet, with a diameter of 4878 km (Figure 2). In size it lies between the Moon and Mars. Its orbit has greater eccentricity (0.205) and inclination to the ecliptic plane (7°) than any other planet except Pluto. This pronounced eccentricity causes the apparent solar intensity at Mercury to vary by more than a factor of two throughout a Mercurian year. Table 1 lists the best current values of the more important orbital and physical properties of the planet.

Table 1   Orbital and Physical Data for Mercury

Orbital Data	
Semimajor axis	0.3871 AU (5.79×10^7 km)
Perihelion distance	0.3075 AU (4.60×10^7 km)
Aphelion distance	0.4667 AU (6.98×10^7 km)
Sidereal period	87.97 days
Synodic period	115.88 days
Orbital eccentricity	0.20563
Inclination of orbit to ecliptic	7.004 deg
Mean orbital velocity	47.87 km/s
Rotational period	58.646 days

Physical Data	
Radius	2439 km
Surface area	7.475×10^7 km^2
Volume	6.077×10^{10} km^3
Mass	3.302×10^{26} g
Mean density	5.44 g/cm^3
Surface gravity	370 cm/s^2
Escape velocity	4.25 km/s
Surface temperature extremes	~100 to 700°K (−173 to 427°C)
Normal albedo	0.125
Magnetic dipole moment	$4.8 (\pm 0.5) \times 10^{22}$ gauss cm^3

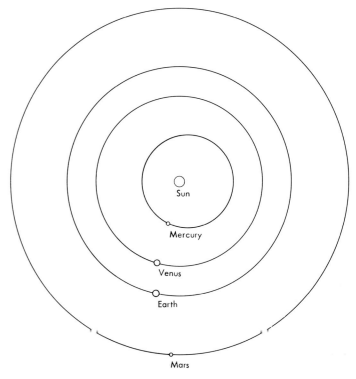

Figure 1   Orbits of the terrestrial planets.

The best Earth-based and Mariner 10 measurements indicate that the rotation period (58.64 days) is in two-thirds resonance with the orbital period (87.97 days), as shown schematically in Figure 3. Therefore, at Mercury's equator, longitudes 0° and 180° are subsolar points near alternate perihelion passages and are called "hot poles," whereas equatorial longitudes 90° and 270° are subsolar points near alternate aphelion passages and are called "warm poles" because they receive less solar energy per "day" on Mercury (175 terrestrial days) than do the "hot poles." The equatorial temperatures vary from about 100°K at local midnight to 700°K at local noon at perihelion, or a range of 600°K during a Mercurian "day." This temperature range is greater than that of any other planet or satellite in the solar system.

In the past, Earth-based observations at visible, infrared, and microwave wavelengths led most observers to conclude that the Mercurian atmosphere was, at best, tenuous, with a total pressure < 0.1 mb. Mariner 10's ultraviolet spectroscopy and radio science experiments confirmed this inference, but extended the upper limit estimates downward by seven orders of magnitude to 10^{-12} bar. A very thin (10^{-15} bar) helium atmosphere was detected, and the question of its origin is now under discussion.[5] The natural decay of uranium and thorium in crustal rocks may have resulted in the generation of the helium, or it may have accreted from the solar wind. If the observed helium is internally generated, then a crustal thickness can be estimated.

Before the Mariner 10 mission, it was generally believed that, because of Mercury's slow rotation and presumed interaction with the solar wind, its magnetic field would be similar to that of the Moon. One of the most important discoveries made by Mariner 10 on its first encounter with Mercury was the existence of a planet-related magnetic field, as indicated by the detection of a bow shock and magnetosphere together with accelerated protons and electrons in the interaction region. The first encounter data did not give a unique answer on the origin of the magnetic field, i.e., whether it was internally generated or induced by a complex interaction with the solar wind. However, Mariner 10's third Mercury encounter provided strong evidence that the field is of internal origin.[6] The magnetic field data obtained during the third encounter duplicated those predicted on the basis of an intrinsic field model. Furthermore, the correlative plasma data showed the Mercurian magnetosphere to be a scaled-down (1/30) replica of the Earth's.[7] Therefore, Mercury has an intrinsic dipole magnetic field with a moment 4×10^{-4} that of the Earth's dipole moment. The maximum field intensity is 400 gammas, or 20 times larger than the interplanetary field at Mercury's distance from the Sun.[6]

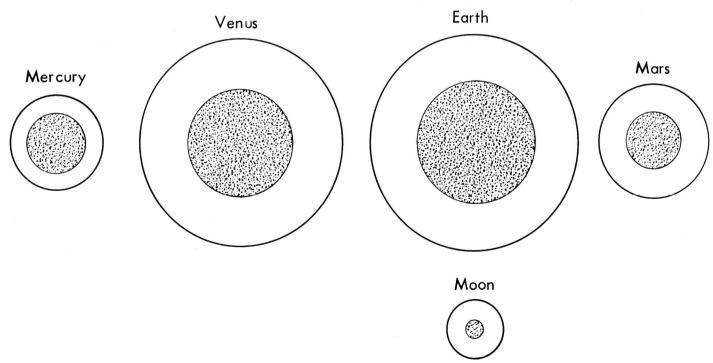

Figure 2   Relative sizes of the Moon and terrestrial planets. Their approximate core sizes are indicated by the stippling.

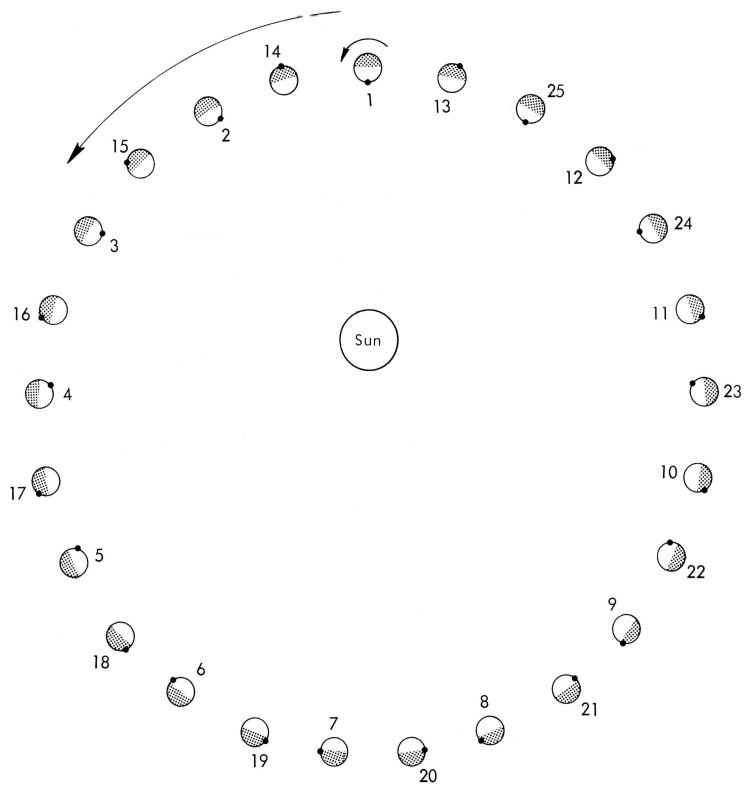

Figure 3 Mercury rotates on its axis three times while it circles the Sun twice. This synchronous rotation can be followed in the schematic diagram by observing the position of the dot (which represents a fixed point on Mercury's surface) as the planet moves from position 1 to 2, 2 to 3, ..., 25 to 1.

The precise mechanism for field generation remains unknown, as fossil magnetization and an active internal dynamo cannot be distinguished from the data. The magnetic field observations provide independent evidence that Mercury possesses a large, metal-rich core.

Probably the most anomalous property of Mercury is its high mean density of 5.44 g/cm^3, which is comparable to that of the Earth (5.52 g/cm^3). However, Mercury is only about one-third the size of the Earth; its uncompressed average density of 5.3 is considerably greater than that of the Earth (4.04). This indicates that Mercury is composed of 65 to 70 percent by weight of metal phase (probably iron), and only some 30 percent by weight of silicate phase. Therefore, Mercury apparently contains twice as much iron (in terms of percentage composition) as any other planet in the solar system. Measurements of the magnetic field and evidence of volcanism in the Mariner 10 photography suggest that Mercury is chemically differentiated.[8] If this is correct and most of the iron is concentrated in a core, then the core volume is about 50 percent of the total volume, and its radius is about 70 to 80 percent of the radius of the planet.

As a consequence of Mercury's high mean density, its surface gravity (370 cm/s^2) is virtually the same as that of Mars, although it is considerably smaller. The gravity scaling of surface processes is the same for both bodies.

The photometric, polarimetric, and thermal properties of Mercury derived from Earth-based measurements are very similar to those of the Moon and indicate a surface covered by a dark, porous, fine-grained particulate layer.[9] The thermal properties of the Mercurian surface measured by the Mariner 10 infrared radiometer are also consistent with the presence of a lunar-like regolith of insulating silicate particles constituting at least the upper tens of centimeters. However, spatial variations in the thermophysical properties of this layer suggest large-scale regions of enhanced thermal conductivity which could be areas of more compacted soil, or areas in which boulders or outcroppings of rock are exposed.[10]

The best Earth-based telescopic photographs of Mercury have a resolution of about 700 km. These photographic and visual observations show that the surface of Mercury consists of dark and light regions somewhat similar to the maria and highlands of the Moon seen at comparable resolution. Although radar altitude profiles and reflectivity maps in the equatorial regions suggested the presence of a cratered surface, it was not known before the Mariner 10 mission that the topography was similar to that of the Moon.[11] Most planetologists believed that Mercury would show a cratered surface, although the amount of cratering was in dispute. Some believed that the crater density would be much less than that on the Moon or Mars because of Mercury's great distance from the asteroid belt, whereas others believed it would show a crater density comparable to that of the Moon. Questions concerning the presence or absence of volcanism, the tectonic framework, and the surface history were unresolved.

Mariner 10 dispelled many mysteries about Mercury and exposed its surface to detailed studies previously possible only for the Moon and Mars. The best pictures of Mercury acquired by Mariner 10 have a resolution of 100 m, an improvement by a factor of about 7000 over Earth-based resolution. As demonstrated by the pictures contained in this Atlas, the tremendous increase in resolution has resulted in a quantum jump in man's knowledge of the planet.

Mariner 10 Mission and Spacecraft

The Mariner 10 spacecraft was launched on the first day of the scheduled launch period, November 3, 1973, at 0045 Eastern Standard Time (0545 Greenwich Mean Time) from Cape Canaveral, Florida, using an Atlas/Centaur D1-A launch vehicle.[12] The spacecraft received a gravity assist from Venus on February 5, 1974 and encountered Mercury on March 29, 1974, 146 days after launch (Figure 4). The exploration of Mercury was the primary objective of the mission and the basis for the selection of the Mariner 10 experiment complement. Experimenters wished to determine, at least in general terms, several of the important properties of this little-known planet. In particular, it was desired to ascertain the nature of Mercury's surface morphology; whether an atmosphere is present, and, if so, the constituents; the planet's interaction with the solar wind; and a refinement of its mass and radius. Because solar wind data can provide important information on a planet's bulk properties, the study of the interaction between Mercury and the solar wind was given a high scientific priority, and a dark-side passage at 705 km altitude was selected for the flyby.

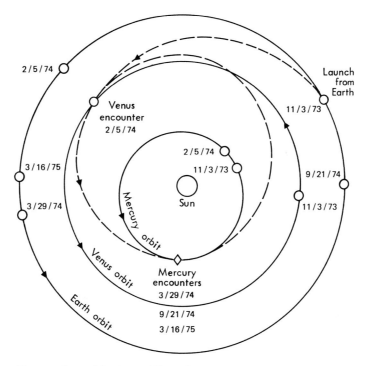

Figure 4   Mariner 10 trajectory.

An aim point within the solar occultation zone made possible a sensitive search for a tenuous neutral atmosphere by observation of the extinction of solar extreme ultraviolet radiation and by a favorable ground-track for studying the infrared thermal emission of the surface from midafternoon to midmorning, local time. Mariner 10 passed through the region in which Earth is occulted by Mercury (as viewed from the spacecraft) to permit a dual-frequency (X- and S-band) radio occultation probe in search of an ionosphere and to measure the radius of the planet.

After completing a 176-day solar orbit following its first Mercury flyby, the Mariner 10 spacecraft successfully encountered Mercury for a second time on September 21, 1974 (Figure 4). The reencounter was at the same position in the solar system, 0.46 AU from the Sun. The spacecraft passed by the sunlit side of Mercury at an altitude of 48,069 km. The main objective of this second flyby was to extend the photographic coverage of Mercury. The new photographs obtained were used to tie together the incoming and outgoing portions of Mercury photographed during the first encounter and provided new views of the south polar area.

Mariner 10 passed Mercury for the third time on March 16, 1975, at 327 km altitude. This encounter yielded the most accurate celestial mechanics data of the mission because of the close passage and the absence of an Earth occultation. The main objective of the third encounter was to define the source of the weak magnetic field discovered on the first encounter. Like the first encounter, it was a dark-side pass. Photographs at a resolution of about 100 m were obtained during the third encounter. Partial-frame pictures were acquired in areas not previously photographed at this resolution.

THE SPACECRAFT

Figure 5 is a schematic of the Mariner 10 spacecraft. The weight of the spacecraft was 504 kg, which included 20 kg of hydrazine fuel and 79.4 kg of scientific experiments. When fully deployed, the spacecraft measured 3.7 m from the top of the low-gain antenna to the bottom of the heat shield of the thrust vector control assembly of the propulsion subsystem. Its total span was 8.0 m with the two solar panels extended. Each panel measured 2.69 m long and 0.97 m wide and was attached to outriggers on the octagonal bus. The high-gain antenna, magnetometer boom, and the plasma science experiment boom also were attached to the bus. The two-degrees-of-freedom scan platform contained the two television cameras and the ultraviolet airglow spectrometer.

The high-gain antenna was an aluminum, honeycombed parabolic dish reflector antenna 1.37 m in diameter with a focal distance of 0.55 m. Right-handed, circularly polarized radiating feeds were attached to the antenna to allow transmission at both S-band (2295 MHz) and X-band (8415 MHz) frequencies. Transmissions from Earth were received at an S-band frequency of 2113 MHz. The antenna was attached to a deployable support boom and was driven by two-degrees-of-freedom actuators to obtain optimum pointing toward Earth.

SCIENTIFIC EXPERIMENTS

The scientific experiments (Table 2) were selected to take advantage of the opportunity to encounter Mercury and to approach the Sun more closely than ever before. The television science and infrared radiometry experiments provided measurements of the surface of the planet. The plasma science, charged particles, and magnetic field experiments supplied measurements of the environment around the planet and the interplanetary medium. The dual-frequency radio science and ultraviolet spectroscopy experiments were designed for detection and measurement of the characteristics of Mercury's neutral atmosphere and ionosphere. The celestial mechanics experiment provided measurements of planetary mass characteristics and tests of the theory of relativity. Although all experiments were designed and selected to achieve the scientific objectives at Mercury, important data were obtained during the Venus encounter and during the cruise phase. The arrangement of these experiments on the spacecraft is shown in Figure 5.

Television Science. Because Mariner 10's trajectory at Mercury passed through the solar occultation regions (Figure 6), the closest approach to the planet occurred

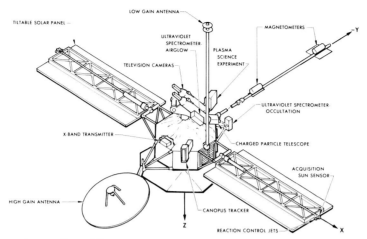

Figure 5   The Mariner 10 spacecraft.

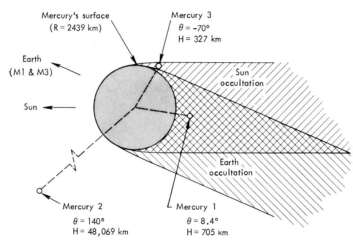

Figure 6   Mercury flyby points.

when the cameras could not see the sunlit portion of Mercury. Consequently, the cameras were equipped with 1500-mm focal length lenses so that high-resolution pictures could be taken during the approach and post-en-

---

Table 2   Mariner 10 Scientific Experiments

Experiment	Principal Investigator	Institution	Instrument
Television science	B. C. Murray	California Institute of Technology	Twin 1.5 m telescopes, vidicon cameras
Infrared radiometry	C. S. Chase	Santa Barbara Research Corporation	Infrared radiometer
Ultraviolet spectoscopy	A. L. Broadfoot	Kitt Peak National Observatory	Airglow spectrometer and occulation spectrometer
Celestial mechanics and radio science	H. T. Howard	Stanford University	X-band transmitter
Magnetic field	N. F. Ness	Goddard Space Flight Center	Two triaxial fluxgate magnetometers
Plasma science	H. S. Bridge	Massachusetts Institute of Technology	Scanning electrostatic analyzer and electron spectrometer
Charged particles	J. A. Simpson	University of Chicago	Charged particle telescope

counter phases. The schematic view of the television camera is shown in Figure 7, and the camera characteristics are given in Table 3.

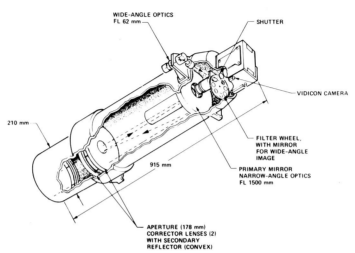

Figure 7   Schematic view of Mariner 10 television camera.

The imaging sequence was initiated 7 days before the encounter with Mercury when about half of the illuminated disk was visible and the resolution was better than that achievable with Earth-based telescopes. Photography of the planet continued until some 30 min before closest approach, providing a smoothly varying sequence of pictures of increasing resolution and decreasing areal coverage. Pictures with resolutions on the order of 2 to 4 km were obtained for both quadratures on the first encounter (Figures 18 and 19). Variation in resolution, ranging between several hundred kilometers to approximately 100 m, assisted in the extrapolation of large-scale features observed at high resolution over broad areas photographed at lower resolution. The highest resolution photographs were obtained approximately 30 min prior to and following closest approach on the first and third encounters. Pictures taken in a number of spectral bands enabled the determination of regional color differences.

The second Mercury encounter (Figure 6) provided a unique opportunity to observe regions of Mercury with more favorable viewing geometry than was possible during the first encounter. In order to permit a third encounter, it was necessary to target the bright-side encounter for a south polar pass. This trajectory allowed unforeshortened views of the south polar region, the exploration of areas not previously accessible for study, a geologic and cartographic tie in the southern hemisphere between the two sides of Mercury photographed on the first encounter,

and the acquisition of stereoscopic coverage of the southern hemisphere. Because of the small field of view resulting from the long focal length optics, it was necessary to increase the periapsis altitude to about 48,000 km to ensure sufficient overlapping coverage to make a reliable geologic and cartographic tie. The resolution of the photographs taken during closest approach ranged from 1 to 3 km (Figure 20).

Table 3 Television Camera Characteristics	
Focal length	1500 mm (62 mm)[a]
Focal number	f/8.4
Shutter speed range	33.3 ms to 11.7 s
Angular field of view	$0.38° \times 0.47°$ ($9° \times 11°$)[a]
Vidicon target image area	9.6×12.35 mm
Scan lines per frame	700
Image elements per line	832
Bits per image element	8
Frame time	42 s
Spectral filters	Blue, ultraviolet, ultraviolet polarizing, orange, minus ultraviolet, and clear

[a]Wide-angle optics.

The third Mercury encounter was targeted to optimize the acquisition of magnetic and solar wind data. Therefore, the viewing geometry on the third encounter was very similar to that on the first encounter. However, the third encounter presented the opportunity to target high-resolution pictures to areas of geologic interest seen previously at lower resolution. Because of ground communication problems, these pictures were acquired as quarter frames.

Infrared Radiometry. The primary goal of the infrared radiometry experiment was to measure infrared thermal radiation emanating from the surface of Mercury between late afternoon and early morning. These temperature measurements taken on the first encounter provided much more accurate values for the average thermal properties of the planet than can be obtained from ground-based studies. An important secondary objective was to search for possible correlations between thermal anomalies and topographic features.

Ultraviolet Spectroscopy. The occultation spectrometer provided a sensitive detection of any atmosphere present, and of its composition, with a detection threshold improved by a factor of about 10^7 over current ground-based studies. The airglow spectrometer provided quantitative information on the abundance of H, He, He[+], C,

O, Ne, and A in the atmosphere of Mercury by measuring the intensity and spatial distribution of their ultraviolet emission lines. Data were taken on the first and third encounters.

Celestial Mechanics and Radio Science. The celestial mechanics experiment provided improved measurements of the mass and gravitational characteristics of Mercury. The planet's close proximity to the Sun, large orbital eccentricity, and unusual spin-orbit resonance made this experiment of primary interest.

The occultation of the spacecraft by Mercury on the first encounter afforded an opportunity to probe the atmosphere and to measure the radius of the planet. Phase changes in the S-band radio signal allowed measurement of an atmosphere with about 10^{16} molecules per cm^3. A more sensitive but less direct measurement of atmospheric gas density was provided by the ionospheric refractivity measurements.

Magnetic Field and Plasma Science. Vector magnetic field and plasma measurements were made to study the interaction of Mercury with the solar wind. Because of the nature of the solar wind and the physical processes under investigation, these phenomena are strongly interrelated and mutually supporting. Data were taken on the first and third encounters.

Charged Particles. The charged particle telescope was designed to detect high-energy particles at Mercury. This experiment complemented and extended the magnetic field and plasma science measurements of the interaction of Mercury with the solar wind.

Topographic Features and Surface History

Although Mercury is remarkably similar to the Moon, it is different from it in many respects. This paradox was not unexpected based on observations from Earth predating the Mariner 10 mission. On the one hand it was known that Mercury reflects sunlight and radar waves in the same manner as does the Moon. This similarity combined with the probable absence of any appreciable atmosphere suggested a cratered surface and a lunar-like regolith of pulverized rock mantling the surface of the planet as the result of meteoritic bombardment. On the other hand, the bulk density of the planet was known to be almost the same as that of Earth and about 60 percent greater than that of the Moon, implying that Mercury was a body greatly enriched in the heavy elements and, like Earth, perhaps having an iron-rich core.

The surface of Mercury, like that of the Moon, was indeed found to be pockmarked with impact craters. However, not expected was the discovery that Mercury, unlike the Moon, has a weak but nevertheless Earth-like magnetic field whose origin is undoubtedly related to a large iron-rich core.[6] Paradoxically, Mercury has a Moon-like exterior and an Earth-like interior.

The illuminated surface observed by Mariner 10 as it first approached Mercury is dominated by craters and basins. This region of Mercury, included in the Victoria, Kuiper, Discovery, and Bach quadrangles (H-2, H-6, H-11, and H-15), shows a heavily cratered surface that at first glance could be mistaken for the lunar highlands. In marked contrast to this view of Mercury, the surface photographed after the flyby, as the spacecraft receded from Mercury, exhibited features totally different from those shown on the incoming views, including large basins and extensive relatively smooth areas with few craters. This coverage fell in the Borealis, Shakespeare, Beethoven, Tolstoj, and Michelangelo quadrangles (H-1, H-3, H-7, H-8, and H-12). The smooth surfaces are clearly younger than the heavily cratered ground seen in the incoming views of Mercury. The most striking feature in this region of the planet is a huge circular basin, 1300 km in diameter, that was undoubtedly produced from a tremendous impact comparable to the event that formed the Imbrium basin on the Moon. This prominent Mercurian structure in the Shakespeare (H-3) and Tolstoj (H-8) quadrangles, named Caloris Planitia, is filled with material forming a smooth surface or plain that appears similar in many respects to the lunar maria. Mercury, much like the Moon, can thus present two totally different faces; one is a heavily cratered surface like the highlands on the back side of the Moon, and the second shows a region of large basins filled with smooth plains similar to the front side of the Moon.[8]

Both the heavily cratered regions of Mercury and the craters themselves, however, differ from their lunar counterparts. Mercury's heavily cratered surfaces exhibit relatively smooth areas or plains between the craters and basins, whereas the lunar highlands display closely packed and overlapping craters. In many cases, these "intercrater" plains appear to predate that time when most of the large Mercurian craters were formed.[8,13] The lunar and Mercurian heavily cratered surfaces are probably different because the force of gravity on Mercury is twice that on the Moon.[14] The ballistic range of material ejected from a primary crater on Mercury is less than that on the Moon and, consequently, covers, depending on the ejection velocity, an area from a fifth to a twentieth smaller for craters of the same size. As a result, ejecta deposits and secondary craters on Mercury are confined more closely around the primary crater than on the Moon; thus, the early cratering record stored in the surface features of Mercury may be better preserved than on the Moon.[14] Ejecta-forming secondaries from the most recent large basin events on the Moon have been superposed on the earlier record of primary craters, increasing the density of craters and obliterating the earlier activity.

The difference in the gravity fields is also probably responsible for the variation in the geometry of craters of the same size on the two bodies.[14] In both cases, the smallest craters are bowl-shaped and with increasing size exhibit central peaks and develop terraces on their inner walls. At the larger sizes, the central peaks become complex structures and undergo a transition into an inner mountain ring that is concentric with the crater rim. Although this progressive change in crater geometry is the same on both the Moon and Mercury, the change from one type to another occurs with smaller diameters on Mercury and apparently reflects gravitationally induced modifications to the original excavation crater.

An additional important difference between the heavily cratered surfaces of Mercury and the Moon are the lobate scarps or cliffs that are several kilometers high and extend for hundreds of kilometers across the Mercurian surface. The scarp named Discovery, by which the H-11 quadrangle is known, is one of the best examples of this feature. Its shape and transection relationships suggest that scarps are thrust faults resulting from compressive stresses, perhaps due to cooling and shrinkage of the iron-rich core, and causing crustal shortening on a global scale.[15] Regardless of the mechanism for forming these escarpments, their presence in the large, well preserved craters establishes an approximate relative time scale for their age and eliminates the possibility that planet-wide melting or Earth-like movement of crustal plates has taken place since the heavily cratered ground was created.

The extensive areas of smooth surfaces or plains on Mercury have been classified into three types.[13] The most widespread type forms a level to gently rolling ground between and around large craters and basins. These "intercrater" plains are characterized by an extremely high density of superposed small (5 to 10 km) craters, which are frequently elongate, shallow, and suggestive of being of secondary origin. A second type, "hummocky" plains, occurs within a broad ring that is 600 to 800 km wide and circumscribes the Caloris Planitia. These plains consist of low, closely spaced to scattered hills, and have been interpreted[13,15] to be material ejected during the cratering event that produced the Caloris basin. "Smooth" plains are the third type and form relatively level tracts with a very low population of craters, both within and external to Caloris Planitia as well as in some of the smaller basins (e.g., Borealis Planitia in the Borealis quadrangle). The smooth plains are similar to the lunar maria and, if analogous, result from extensive lava flows that would reflect an extended period of volcanism on Mercury after the Caloris event.[15,16]

In addition to the cratered surfaces and plains regions, several other distinctive topographic features occur. A system of linear hills and valleys that extends up to 300 km cut through or modify some parts of the heavily cratered and intercrater areas in the Discovery quadrangle (H-11). These valleys are scalloped and range up to 10 km wide. The best example of this type of feature extends more than 1000 km to the northeast from the mountainous rim, Caloris Montes, in the Shakespeare quadrangle (H-3). Both examples are similar to the so-called lunar Imbrium sculpture. It is generally believed that this type of lineated surface feature resulted from excavations by secondary projectiles when the large basins were formed and, possibly, fracturing and faulting of the planet's crust during the basin formation. The basin associated with the lineations in the Discovery quadrangle is unknown, but it may be found in the darkened hemisphere that was hidden from Mariner 10's cameras.[13]

Some of the most peculiar and interesting landforms seen on Mercury are in another region in the Discovery quadrangle that has been termed "hilly and lineated." The hills are 5 to 10 km wide and vary from a few hundred meters up to almost 2 km in height. This region includes many old degraded craters whose rims have been broken up into hills and valleys. Similar surfaces are known at two sites on the Moon. In all three cases, the regions are antipodal to the youngest large basins (Imbrium and Orientale on the Moon and Caloris on Mercury). For this reason, there could be a genetic relationship between the formation of the basins and the hilly and lineated terrain. It has been suggested that seismic waves generated by the basin impacts are focused in the antipodal region and are the cause of the peculiar surfaces.[17]

Well defined bright streaks or ray systems radiating away from craters constitute another distinctive feature of the Mercurian surface, again in remarkable similarity to the Moon. The rays cut across and are superposed on all other surface features, indicating that the source craters are the youngest topographic features on the surface of Mercury.[13] The basin and ray systems are shown in Figure 8.

Despite some differences, the striking duplication of surface features between Mercury and the Moon suggests that although an absolute time scale for the development of the Mercurian surface must remain uncertain, the relative sequence of events for the two bodies must have been very similar, if not contemporary. The greatest uncertainty in the Mercurian absolute time scale is: When did the heavy bombardment forming the heavily cratered surfaces (lunar highlands) and the large basins (lunar Imbrium and Orientale) come to an end?

Within these uncertainties, Mercury's evolution can be divided into five stages or epochs.[8,18] The first epoch includes the interval of time at the earliest stage of the solar system, condensation of the solar nebula into solids, and the accumulation of the solid material into the main mass of Mercury. It is not known whether the planet accumulated heterogeneously or homogeneously; i.e., whether it formed directly as an iron core with a silicate crust, or whether the proto-Mercury was initially a mixture of iron and silicates which subsequently melted and separated into the core and crust configuration. Regardless of how the planet accumulated, all crustal melting must have been completed well before the craters in the heavily cratered surfaces were formed to have preserved their shapes and geometries to the present time. Moreover, if Mercury ever had been enveloped in an atmosphere either during or immediately after accumulation,

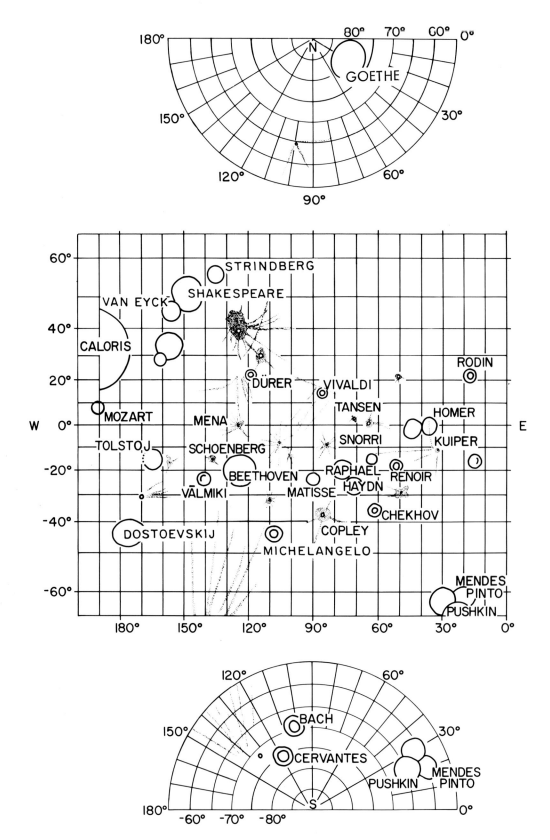

Figure 8   Basin and ray systems.

aeolian degradation of craters would have occurred, similar to that seen on Mars. Because such degradation has not been recognized, any atmosphere must have disappeared before the oldest cratered surfaces were formed.

The second epoch following accumulation and chemical separation was a period of heavy bombardment by large objects from an unknown source that produced the heavily cratered surfaces and the large basins; this epoch was terminated by the time of the Caloris event. It is not certain whether this last period of heavy bombardment was the terminal phase of the accumulation of Mercury, or whether it was a second episode of bombardment unrelated to the accretionary phase.[19] The "intercrater" plains probably represent an older surface that predates this second epoch,[20] or they may have been emplaced during the period of heavy bombardment. Because the lobate scarps are prevalent in the intercrater areas and sometimes pass through and deform some of the older craters, core shrinkage and crustal shortening may have occurred during the end of the first epoch and extended into at least the early part of the second.

A convenient and well delineated point in Mercury's history is the time of the impact that formed the Caloris basin. This massive event marks the onset of the third epoch. It produced the mountainous ring Caloris Montes and the basin Caloris Planitia, as well as the ejecta deposits and sculpturing of the older heavily cratered surface that can be traced more than 1000 km from the ring of mountains. If the Caloris basin were contemporary with the Moon's two youngest basins, Imbrium and Orientale, an absolute time for the Caloris event would be about 4 billion years ago.

The start of the fourth epoch followed an indeterminate, but probably short, period after the Caloris event. During this time broad plains were formed, most probably as a result of widespread volcanism grossly similar to that which produced the lunar maria. It has been suggested, however, that the smooth plains surrounding the Caloris Planitia (i.e., the Suisei, Odin, and Tir Planitia) are ejecta from Caloris that were melted by the impact.[21] If the smooth plains are analogous to lunar maria, this fourth epoch may represent the period of time from 4 to 3 billion years ago. If the plains are impact melt, they must be contemporary with the Caloris event, about 4 billion years in age.

The fifth and final epoch in what can be recognized in Mercurian history probably extends from about 3 billion years ago to the present. Little has happened on Mercury during this period except for a light "dusting" of meteoritic debris which has produced many of the prominent rayed craters. The crater population on the smooth plains is very similar to that on the lunar maria.

The apparent similarity in the sequence of events for the Moon and Mercury is especially significant for interpreting and understanding evolutionary processes of the terrestrial planets. It is now clear that Mercury, in common not only with the Moon, but also with Mars, was subjected to an early, intense crater-producing bombardment (including basin events) that was followed by volcanism and, in turn, by a greatly reduced impact flux. Because the orbital distances to the Sun for these three bodies are significantly different, their cratering records suggest that a similar impact history is basic to all terrestrial planets. If this is correct, then an important step has been made in developing a theory of the origin and evolution of the planets. By implication, for example, the Earth in its early history must also have displayed a surface of craters and basins. Thus, from the observations of Mariner 10 there is evolving a new, more complete and unified understanding of our own planet and the solar system in general.

Surface Mapping

MAP PROJECTIONS

Many different projections are used in making maps; the choice depends on the purpose of the map and the type of distortions which can be tolerated.[22] Some form of distortion is always present when a sphere or spheroid is mapped into a plane, and the selection of the best projection for a particular cartographic product must reflect a compromise of the allowed distortions and the use of the map. Most map projections are designed to give a proper representation of distance (equidistance), shape (conformal), or area (equivalence); however, a projection cannot possess more than one of these properties.

There are three common projection surfaces—the cylinder, the cone, and the plane. Normally the cylinder is tangent to the sphere at the equator; sometimes, however, the transverse or oblique positions are used. With the transverse position the line of tangency is at a selected meridian; with the oblique position the line of tangency is at an angle to the equator and all meridians. When a conical surface is used, it is generally either tangent to the sphere along a particular latitude or it cuts the sphere along two lines of latitude. When a plane is used as a projection surface, it is usually tangent to the sphere at a single point such as the north or south pole.

Over the centuries a great many projections have been devised and employed in making maps of the Earth and its many regions. Land-water boundaries, political areas, roads, or cities are frequently of primary interest. For other planets, these considerations are irrelevant and the center of interest is mainly in the topographic forms and positions. Because it is important to represent accurately the shapes of the topographic features, the map projection should be conformal. Computers are frequently used to project a picture or mosaic into a map. If the projection is conformal, the craters will be round, thus providing a check on the computer program. All of the maps in this Atlas use conformal projections.

The most popular cylindrical projection is the Mercator, which is conformal; the cylinder is usually oriented tangent to the reference sphere at the equator. The transverse Mercator is becoming increasingly popular for Earth cartography and, together with oblique Mercators, will likely find application on other planets. The Lambert normal conical projection is conformal and is useful with one or two standard parallels in the midlatitudes. The stereographic plane projection is conformal and is commonly used in the polar regions with the point of tangency at the pole. Occasionally this projection has the point of tangency at the equator. It has recently been exploited in special maps of large basins found on the Moon, Mars, and Mercury.

NOMENCLATURE

Since the time of Schiaparelli, a number of astronomers have drawn maps of the surface markings on Mercury; however, only Lowell (1896)[23] and Antoniadi (1934)[1] gave names to the features on their sketches. Lowell's map is shown as Figure 9 and Antoniadi's is presented as Figure 10. To the extent that nomenclature was used prior to the flight of Mariner 10, Antoniadi's was generally accepted.

At the 1973 meeting of the International Astronomical Union, a Working Group for Planetary System Nomenclature was established. Recommendations made by the Task Group for Mercury Nomenclature[24] must be ap-

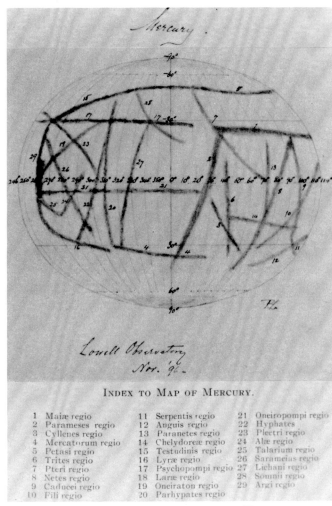

Figure 9 Lowell's map of Mercury.[23]

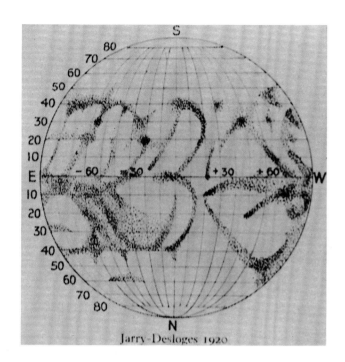

Figure 14 Planisphere of Mercury drawn by Jarry-Desloges in 1920.[27]

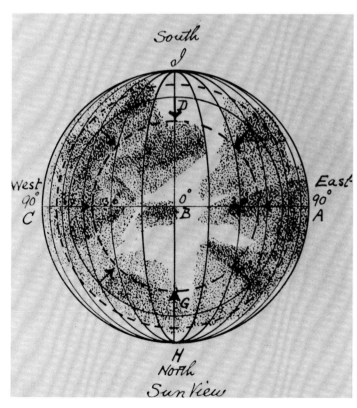

Figure 15 Planisphere of Mercury drawn by H. McEwen.[28]

photographs with those observed by telescope.

The coordinate system used for the Mariner 10 maps of Mercury assumes that the equator lies in the plane of its orbit and that the center of the small crater Hun Kal defines the 20° meridian. The longitudes are measured from 0° to 360°, increasing to the west. The coordinates of the features provided by the control net are used to position the map coordinate grid relative to the topography.[33]

Coordinates of the control points are computed photogrammetrically using a single, large-block, analytical triangulation. The latitude and longitude of the control points and the three orientation angles of the pictures are treated as unknowns in the least-squares computation. The spin axis of Mercury is assumed normal to the orbital plane and the radius at the point is assumed to be constant (usually 2439 km). The trajectory of the spacecraft relative to the center of mass of Mercury was determined by the Jet Propulsion Laboratory navigation team and is assumed to be free from error in the least-squares computation.

Work on the control net started in April 1974, soon after pictures were received from Mercury, and continued for more than 2 years.[34] Points, measurements, and pictures were added, and periodically the triangulation computation was updated. Thus, the coordinates of the control points changed slightly with each computation. The International Astronomical Union (1970) defined the 0° longitude as the subsolar meridian at the first perihelion after January 1, 1950. The control net computations indicate that this definition of longitudes and the Mariner 10 (Hun Kal) definition of longitudes differ by less than 0.5 degree.

Early cartographic work consisted of photomosaics and the start of a 1:5,000,000 series of shaded relief maps made at the U.S. Geological Survey (Branch of Astrogeological Studies, Flagstaff). This series uses 15 different sheets to cover the surface of Mercury, as shown in Figure 16; there are five Mercator projection sheets encircling the planet between north and south 25° latitude, four north and four south Lambert projection sheets between 20° and 70° latitude, and north and south polar stereographic projection sheets between the poles and 65° latitude. The sheets are designated by the letter H (for Hermes; M is used for Mars) followed by a number from 1 to 15. Their names are taken from prominent topographic features in the region. Secondary albedo names (in parentheses) are available for telescopic observers. The north polar stereographic projection is H-1 Borealis (Borea); the north Lambert from 0° to 90° longitude is H-2 Victoria (Aurora); from 90° to 180° longitude is H-3 Shakespeare (Caduceata); from 180° to

270° longitude is H-4 (Liguria); from 270° to 360° longitude is H-5 (Apollonia). The equatorial Mercator is H-6 Kuiper (Tricrena) from longitude 0° to 72°; H-7 Beethoven (Solitudo Lycaonis) from longitude 72° to 144°; H-8 Tolstoj (Phaethontias) from longitude 144° to 216°; H-9 (Solitudo Criophori) from longitude 216° to 288°; and H-10 (Pieria) from longitude 288° to 360°. The southern Lambert sheets are H-11 Discovery (Solitudo Hermae Trismegisti) from longi-

tude 0° to 90°; H-12 Michelangelo (Solitudo Promethei) from longitude 90° to 180°; H-13 (Solitudo Persephones) from longitude 180° to 270°; H-14 (Cyllene) from longitude 270° to 360°; and the south polar stereographic is H-15 Bach (Australia).

The shaded relief maps are used in this Atlas for organizing the pictures and mosaics by region, for indexing, and for referencing names and coordinates.

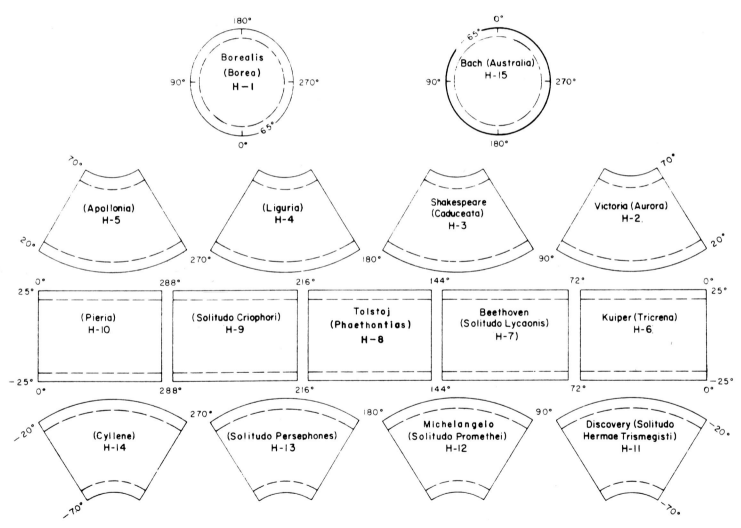

Figure 16   Arrangement of map sheets.

The Atlas

Description

For cartographic purposes, Mercury has been divided into 15 geographical regions (Figure 17). The Mariner 10 television cameras were able to take pictures of the planet's surface corresponding approximately to only 9 of these 15 regions because the same hemisphere was illuminated during all three encounters as a consequence of the synchronous nature of Mercury's rotation and the orbit of the spacecraft around the Sun. This Atlas is divided into 9 sections, each representing one of the cartographic regions. The name and H (prefix for Mercury) number of each region are shown in Figure 17. The regions presented are H-1, H-2, H-3, H-6, H-7, H-8, H-11, H-12, and H-15.

All sections of the Atlas are arranged in the following manner: A 1:5,000,000 shaded relief map and a computer-generated photomosaic are presented first on facing pages for general reference. Subsequent material includes enlargements of portions of the photomosaics, individual high-resolution pictures, mosaics of small areas, and stereo pairs located within the boundaries of the cartographic region. The photomosaics are designated by the letter A for the 1:5,000,000 format and the letters B, C, ... for the enlarged versions (e.g., 1-A, 1-B, ...). Individual pictures, small mosaics, and stereo pairs are designated by a numerical identification (e.g., 1-1, 1-2, ...), where the first digit denotes the cartographic region and the second digit is its identification within the region.

Footprint locations of individual pictures and stereo pairs have been plotted on the shaded relief maps. In cartographic regions H-1 and H-2, where high-resolution, third-encounter photographs were obtained on the planet's limb, footprints are provided both on the limb mosaic and on the shaded relief map. Footprint maps are identified by a 3 unit symbol (e.g., 1-F1, 1-F2, ...), where the first digit denotes the cartographic region and the last two symbols are its identification within the region.

The shaded relief maps are adapted from the 1:5,000,000 series rendered by airbrush artists in the Cartographic Section, Branch of Astrogeological Studies, U.S. Geological Survey (USGS), Flagstaff, Arizona. These maps show the topography without reference to albedo or sun direction, factors which combine to produce a surface appearance often quite different from that in the pictures. Names of surface features and the latitudes and longitudes on the maps make the first page the major reference for each section.

All photo products were produced using computer techniques and software developed in the Image Processing Laboratory (IPL) of the Jet Propulsion Laboratory (JPL), California Institute of Technology. The pictures have been high-pass filtered and contrast enhanced to accentuate surface detail. Pictures used in photomosaics or in stereo pairs have been geometrically transformed to an appropriate projection. A picture element size of 0.4 km was used in the mosaics and a video film converter was used to record the entire photomosaic on 8 by 10 in. film to preserve the resolution inherent in the photographs.

During the first flyby encounter, full coverage of both hemispheres was obtained with a resolution of about 2 km. Individual pictures were processed by IPL and mosaicked by USGS to produce Figure 18, a view of Mercury as seen from the approaching spacecraft, and Figure 19, a view of Mercury as seen from the departing spacecraft.

The second encounter, 6 months later, was on the illuminated side of the planet. Twenty sequences, composed of 18 pictures each, yielded coverage of an area extending from the equator to the south pole and encompassing the south portions of both hemispheres photographed earlier. The pictures were obtained at rapidly changing ranges and viewing angles, thus preventing the combination of the raw photographs into a global mosaic. Therefore, each frame was processed by IPL as an orthographic projection with an origin at $-55°$ latitude and $100°$ longitude. Figure 20 is a mosaic of these pictures and provides a global view of Mercury as seen by the spacecraft as it passed above the point of projection. The only illuminated area not photographed during the three encounters was north of the equator between the limb coverage of the first encounter. This "gore" is especially evident in the H-2 region.

Pictures taken during the third encounter, 1 year after the first visit to the planet, are identified by their strip-like configuration (see, for example, picture 1-13). Very-high-resolution pictures were obtained in specific areas of interest identified during the first pass.

The Caloris basin, bisected by the morning terminator, is the most prominent feature discovered on Mercury. Because of its importance, a special mosaic, Figure 21, was constructed at JPL from the highest resolution pictures of the area obtained during all three encounters. Each photograph was scaled to a similar proportion and additional enhancement matched tone contrast from one picture to another. To eliminate foreshortening and suppress picture edge effects inherent in Figure 21, a stereographic projection was made of the Caloris basin (photomosaic 3-F).

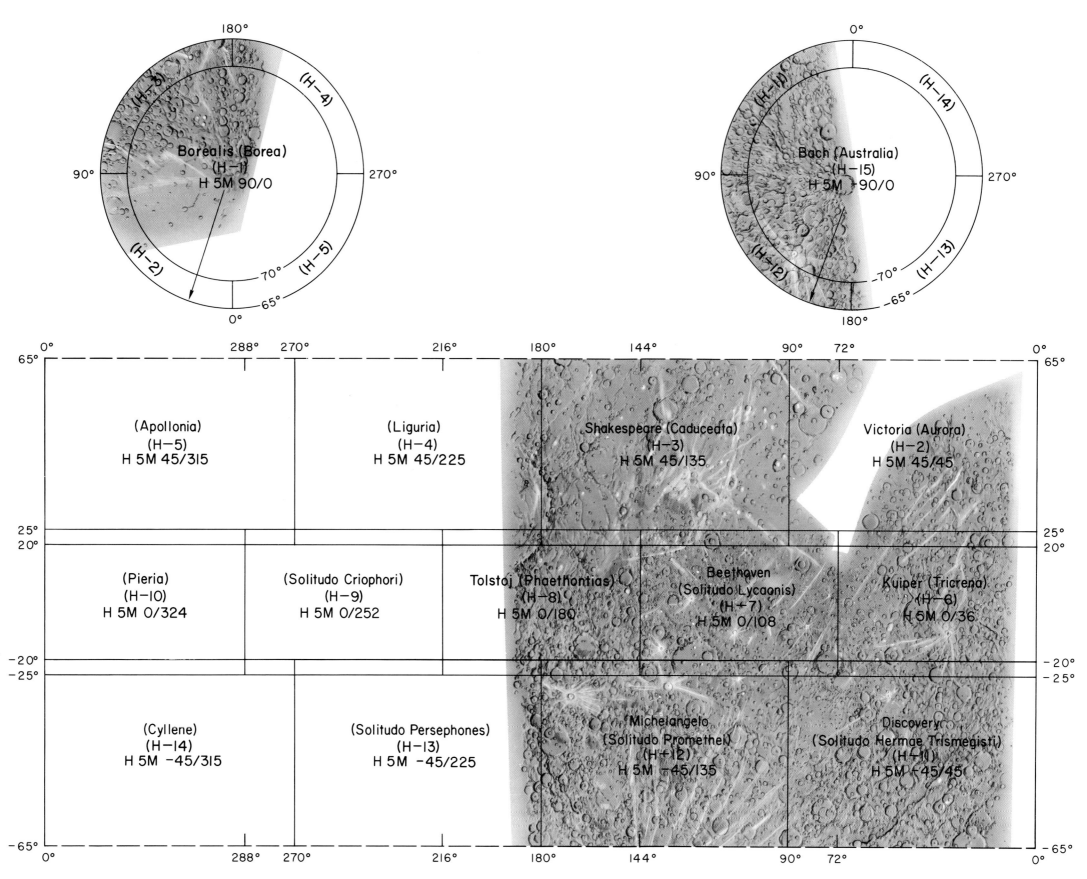

Figure 17 The regions of Mercury as seen by Mariner 10, with the locations of the nine sections of the Atlas indicated

Figure 18   Photomosaic of Mercury as photographed by the approaching spacecraft

Figure 19   Photomosaic of Mercury as photographed by the departing spacecraft

23

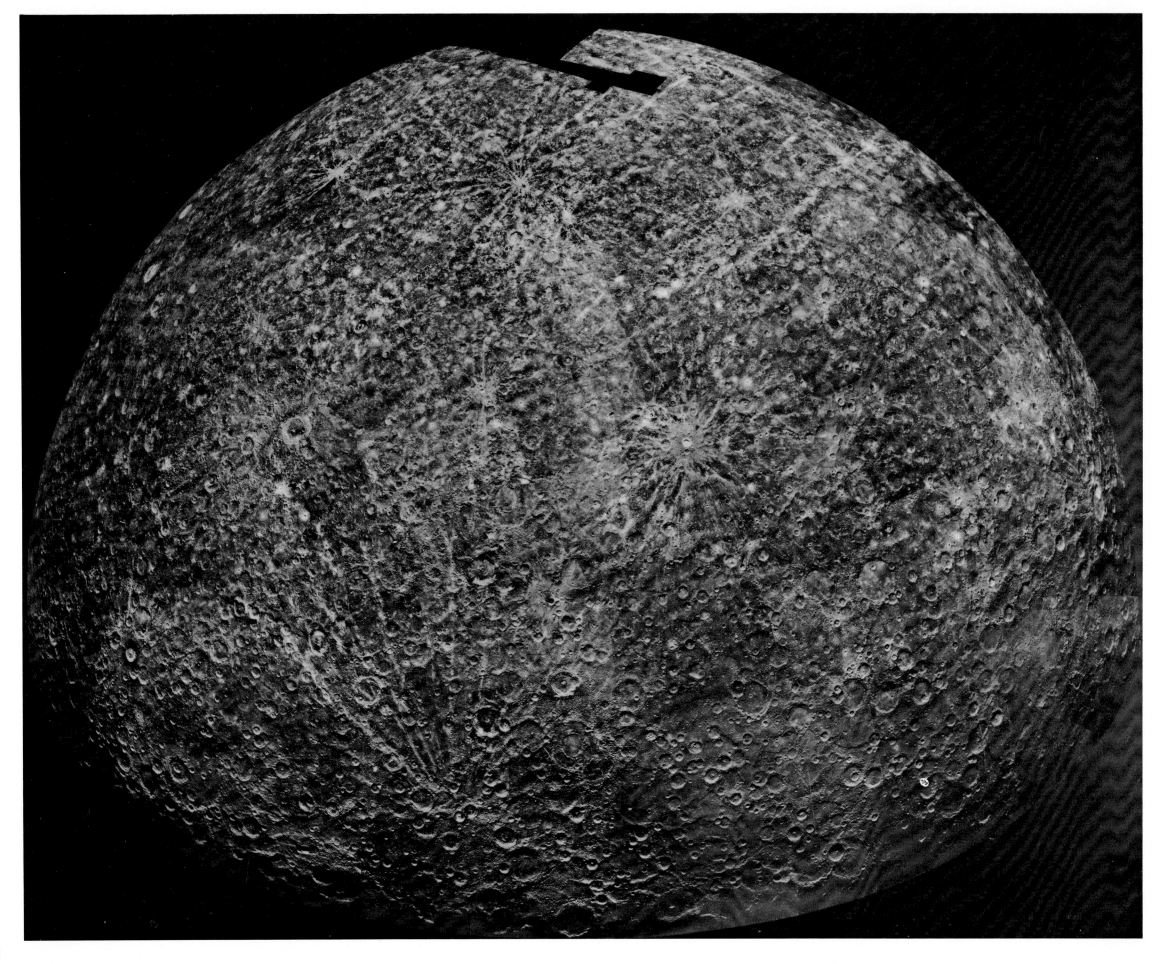

Figure 20   Orthographic photomosaic of the southern hemisphere centered at -55° latitude and 100° longitude

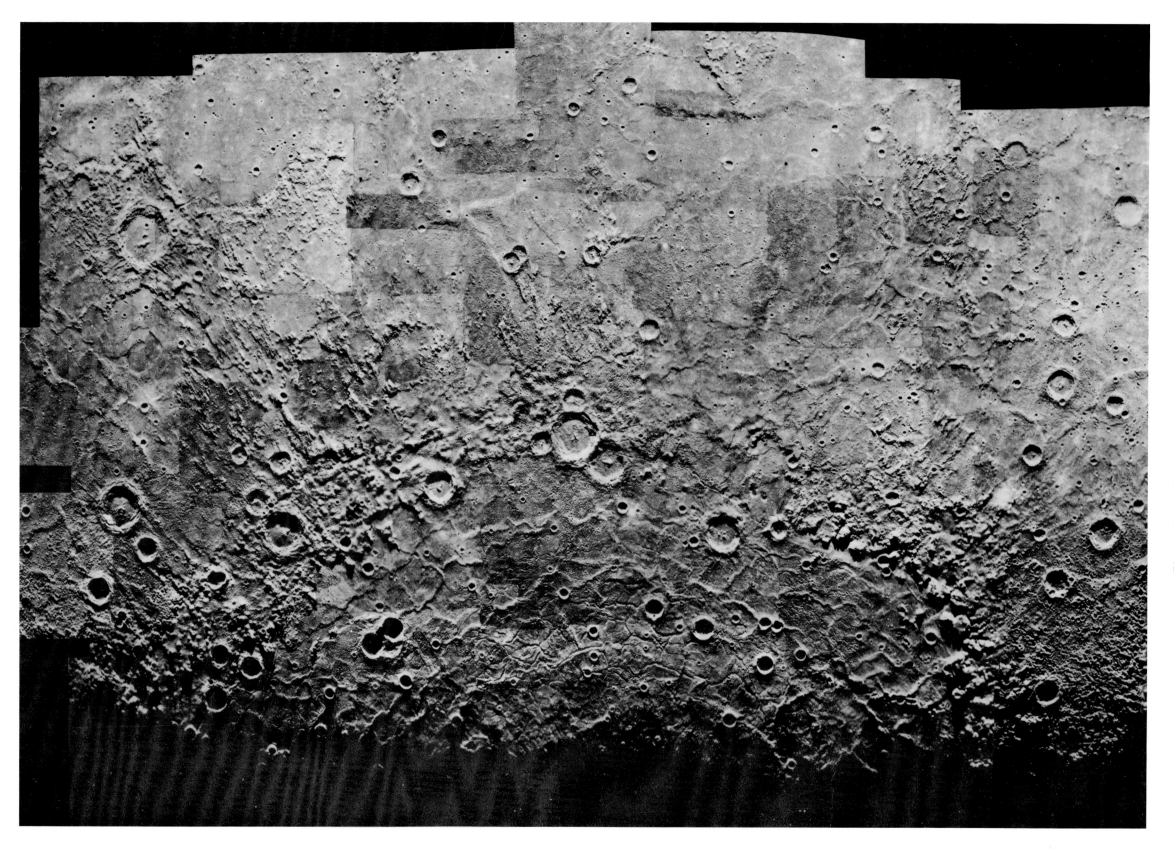

Figure 21   Photomosaic of the Caloris basin

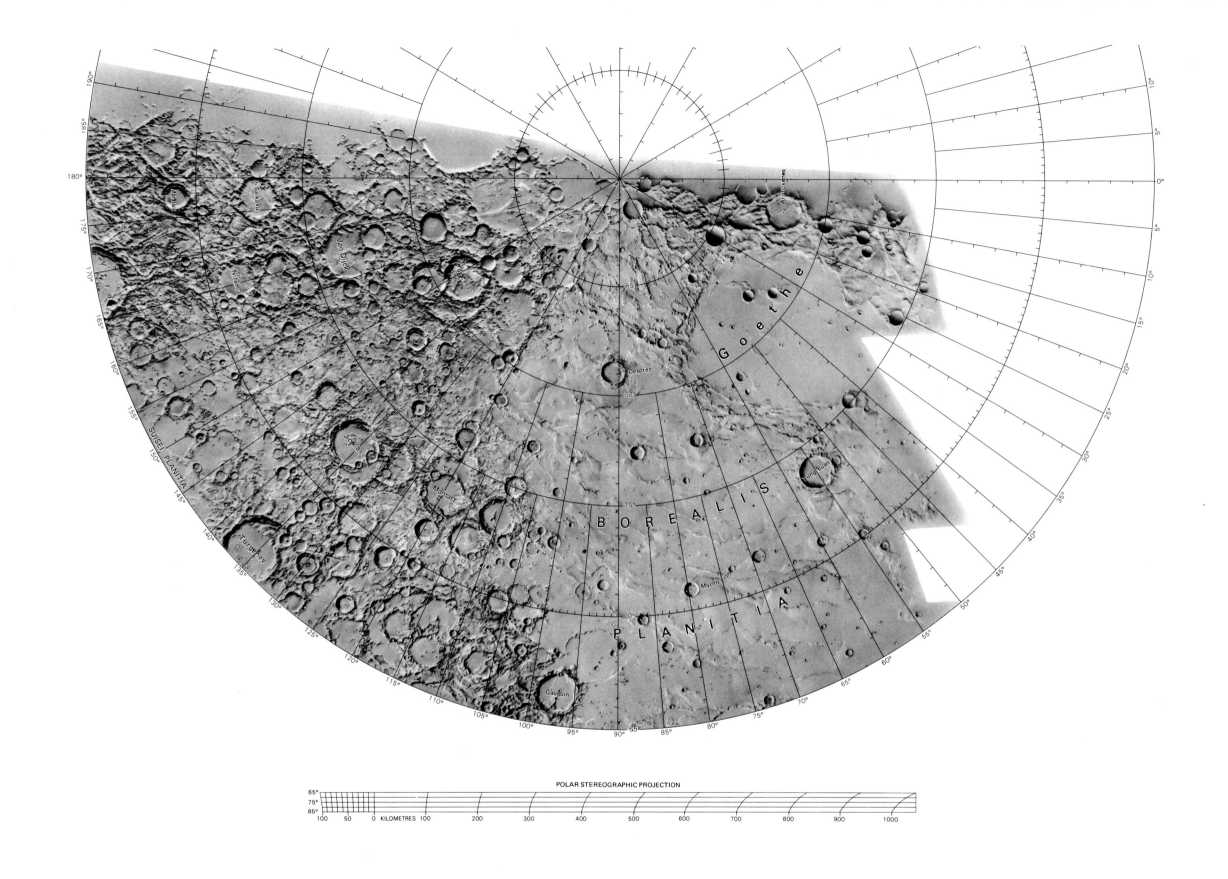

POLAR STEREOGRAPHIC PROJECTION

SHADED RELIEF MAP OF THE BOREALIS QUADRANGLE OF MERCURY
(BOREA ALBEDO PROVINCE)
H-1
H 5M 90 0 R
1977

H1

26

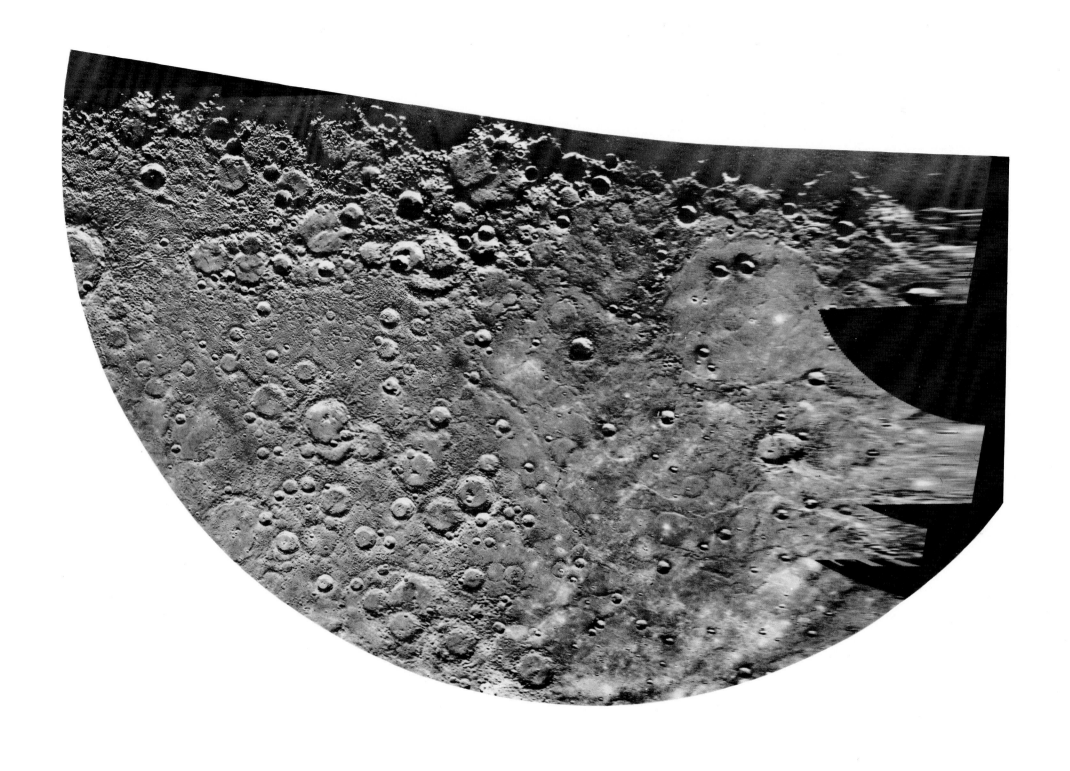

1-A   COMPUTER PHOTOMOSAIC OF THE BOREALIS AREA OF MERCURY

H-1

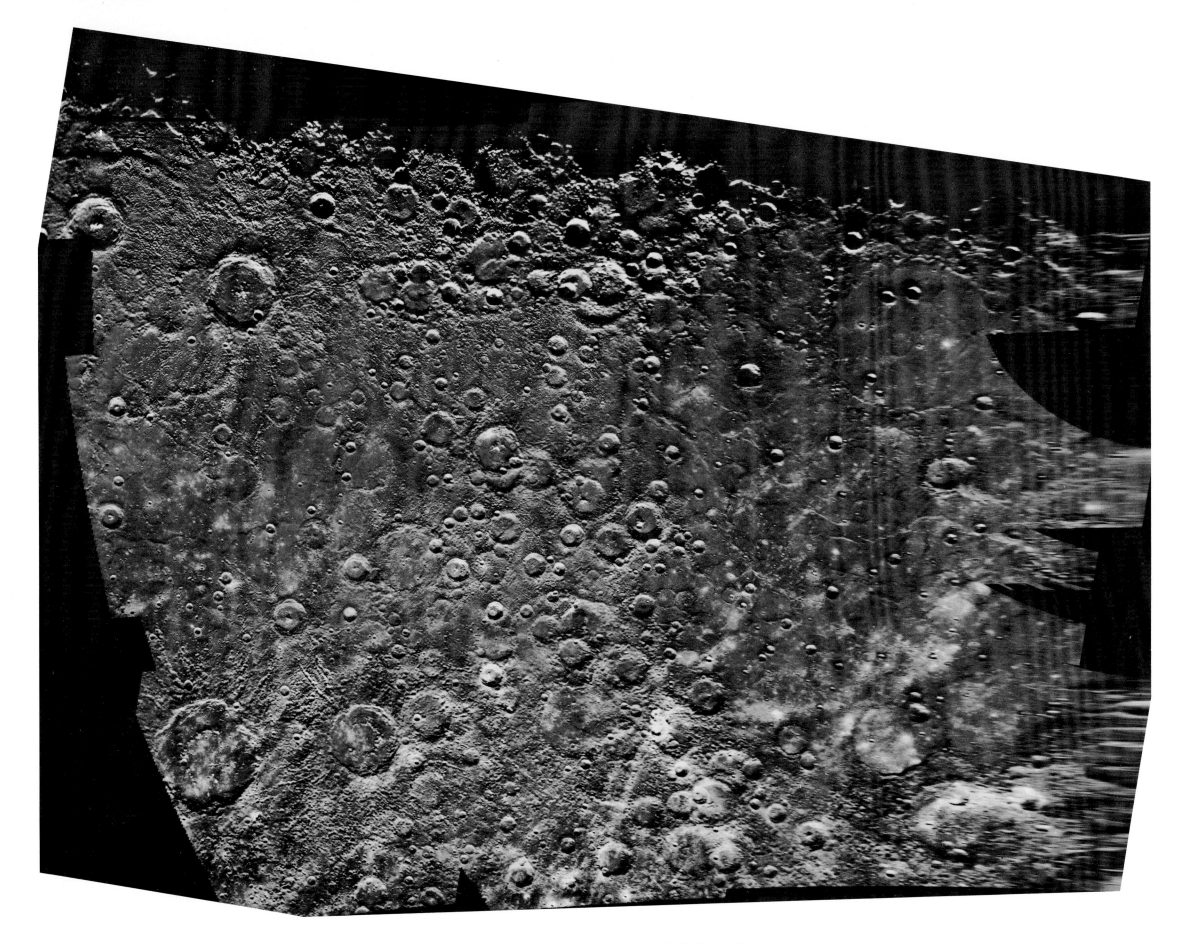

1-B   Enlarged view of the H-1 photomosaic, including adjoining regions

1-F1   Footprints of pictures 1-1 through 1-9 as they appear on the limb

1-1

1-2

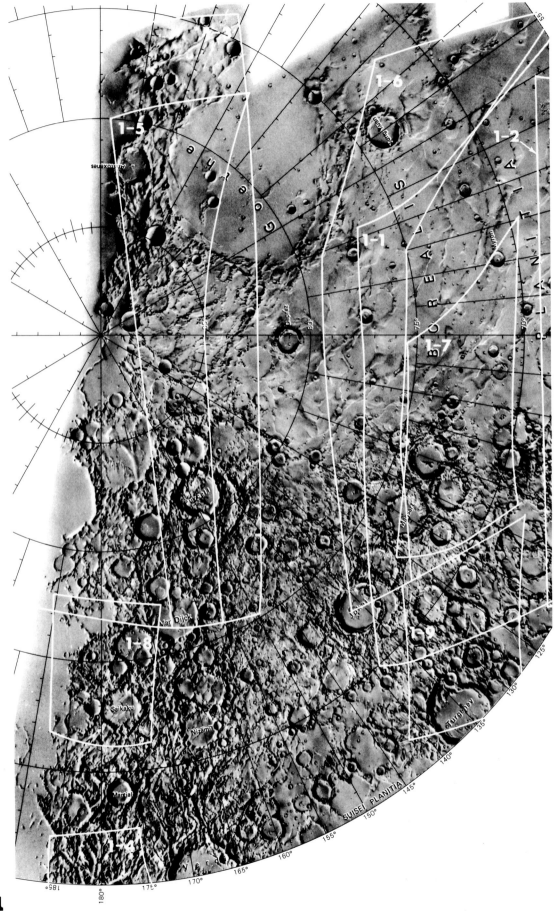

1-F2   Footprints of pictures 1-1 through 1-9 on the shaded relief map

1-3

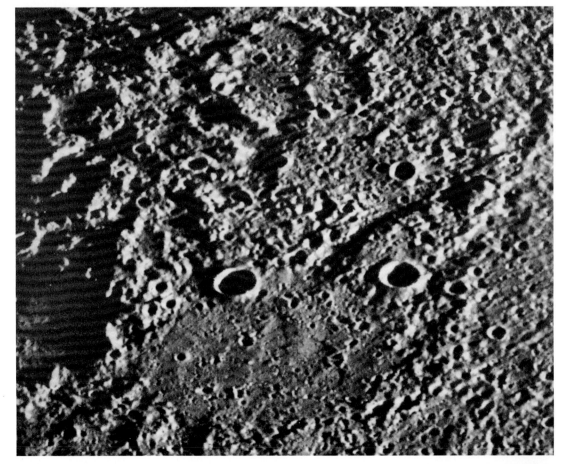

1-4

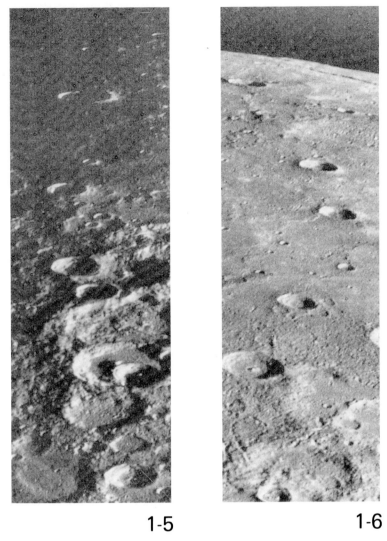

1-5

1-6

1-7

1-8

1-9

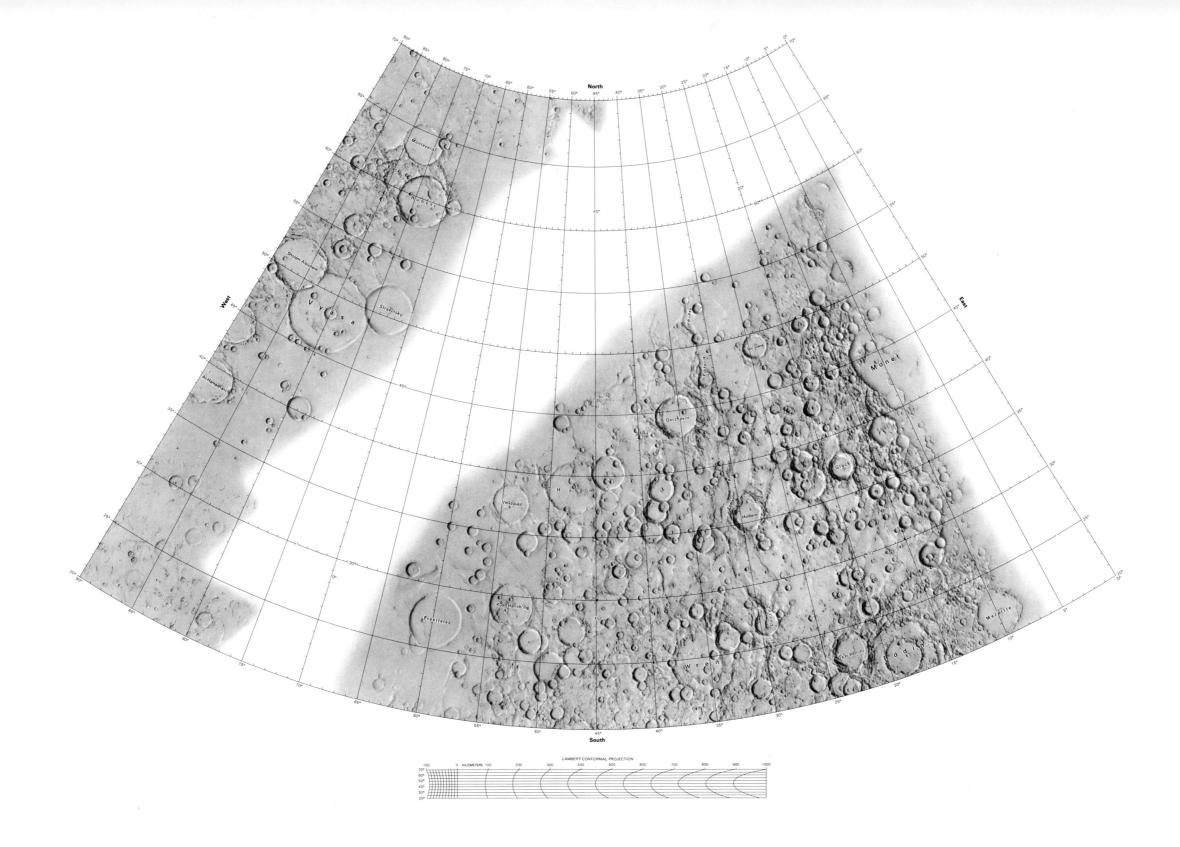

SHADED RELIEF MAP OF THE VICTORIA QUADRANGLE OF MERCURY

(AURORA ALBEDO PROVINCE)

H-2

H 5M 45/45 R

1977

2-A   COMPUTER PHOTOMOSAIC OF THE VICTORIA QUADRANGLE OF MERCURY

H-2

2-B   Enlarged view of the northwest region of the H-2 photomosaic

2-C   Enlarged view of the southeast region of the H-2 photomosaic

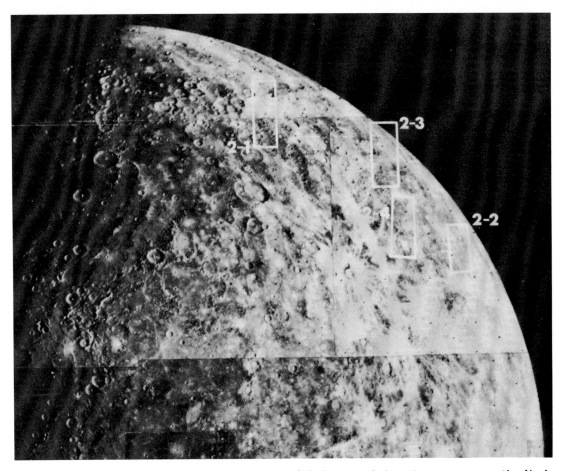

2-F1   Footprints of pictures 2-1 through 2-4 as they appear on the limb.

2-1

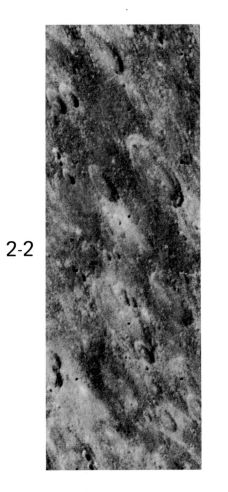

2-2

2-3

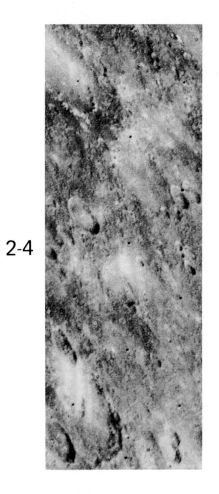

2-4

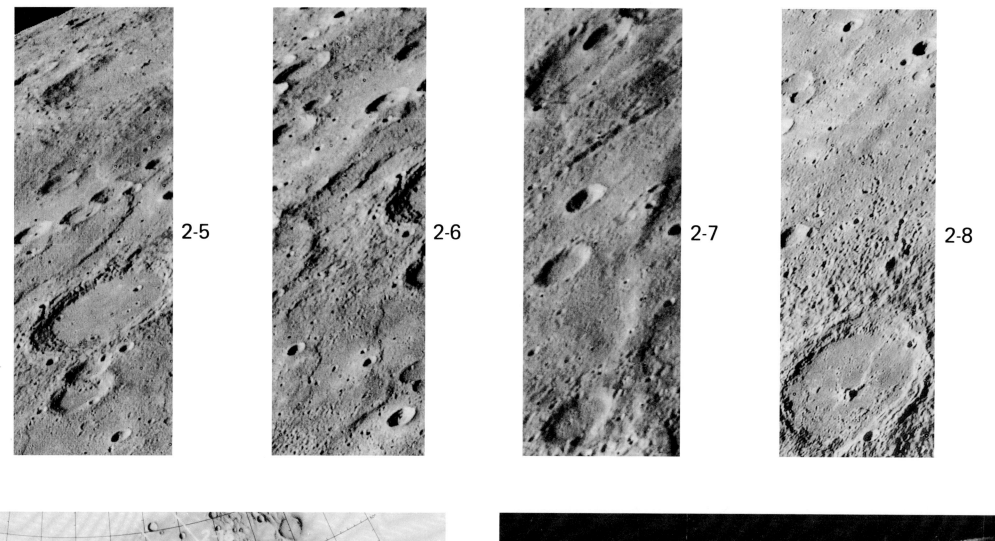

2-5 2-6 2-7 2-8

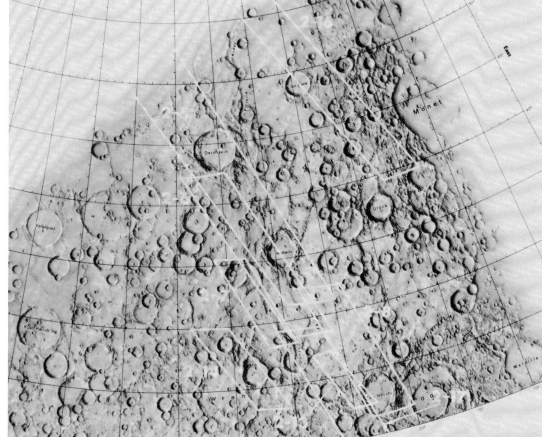

2-F3   Footprints of pictures 2-5 through 2-8, 2-13, 2-14, 2-16, and 2-17 on the shaded relief map.

2-F4   Footprints of these same pictures as they appear on the limb.

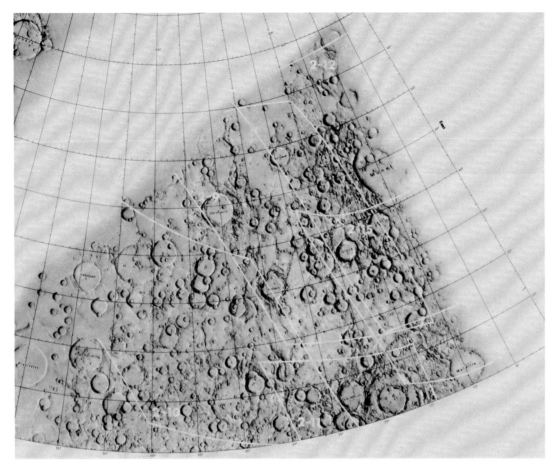

2-F5   Footprints of pictures 2-9 through 2-12 and 2-15 on the shaded relief map.

2-9

2-10

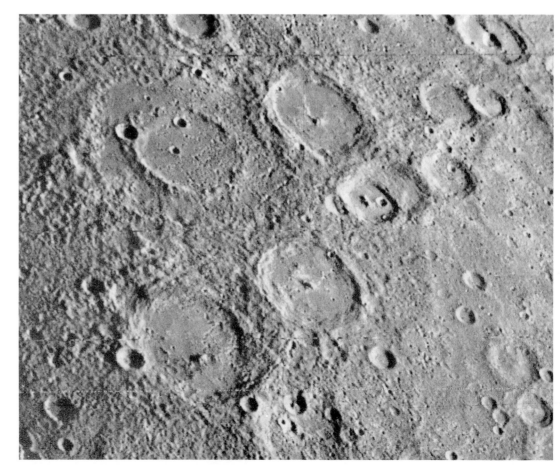

2-11

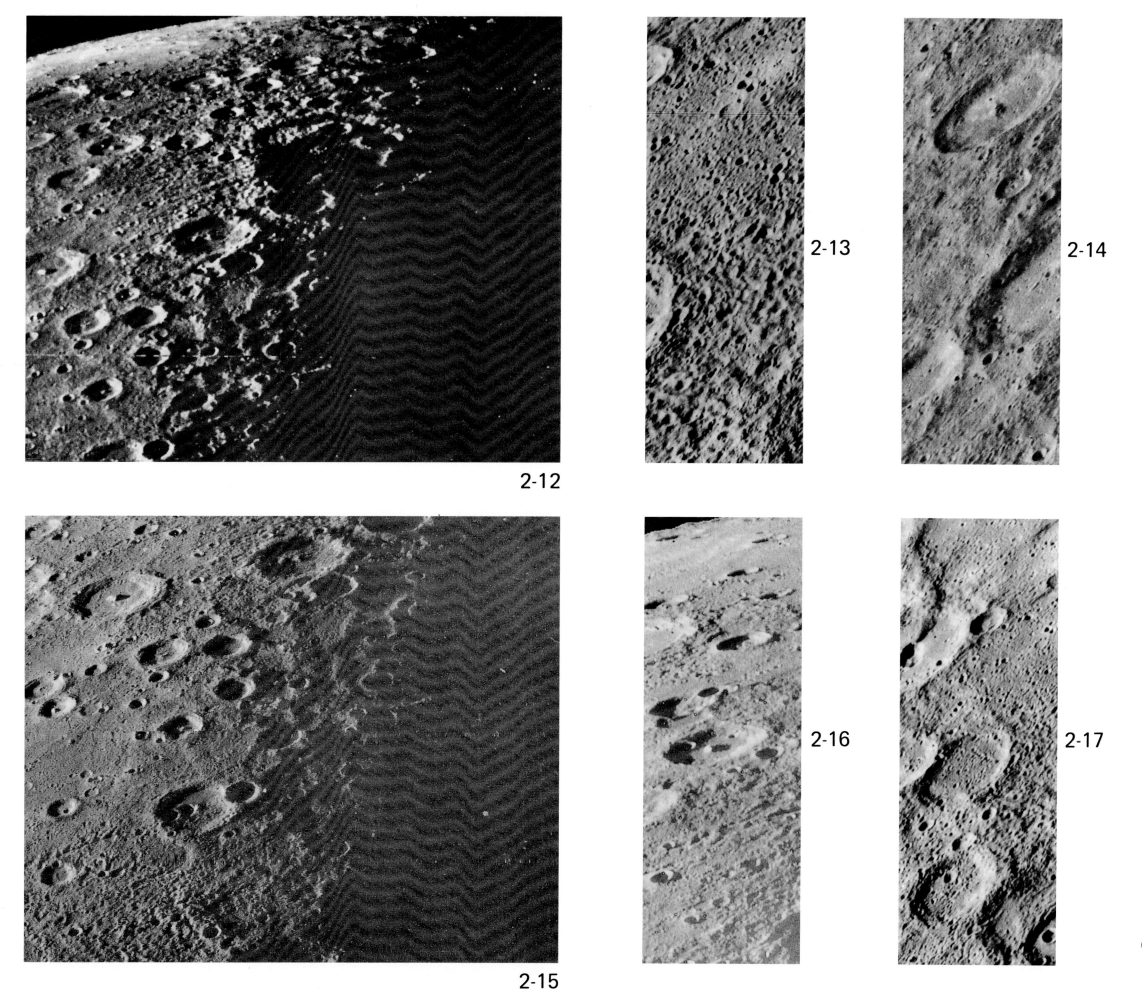

2-12

2-13

2-14

2-15

2-16

2-17

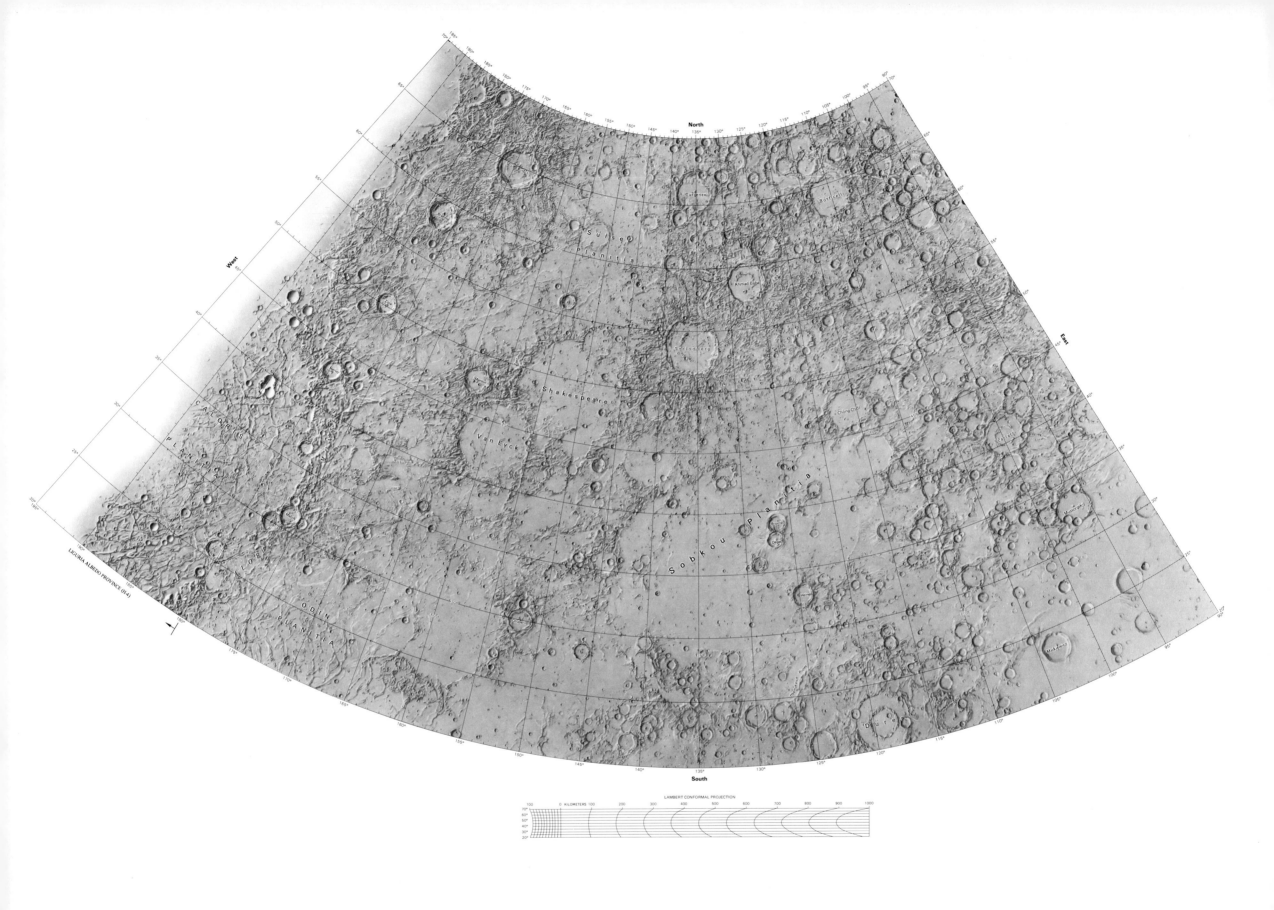

SHADED RELIEF MAP OF THE SHAKESPEARE QUADRANGLE OF MERCURY
(CADUCEATA ALBEDO PROVINCE)
H-3
H 5M 45/135 R
1977

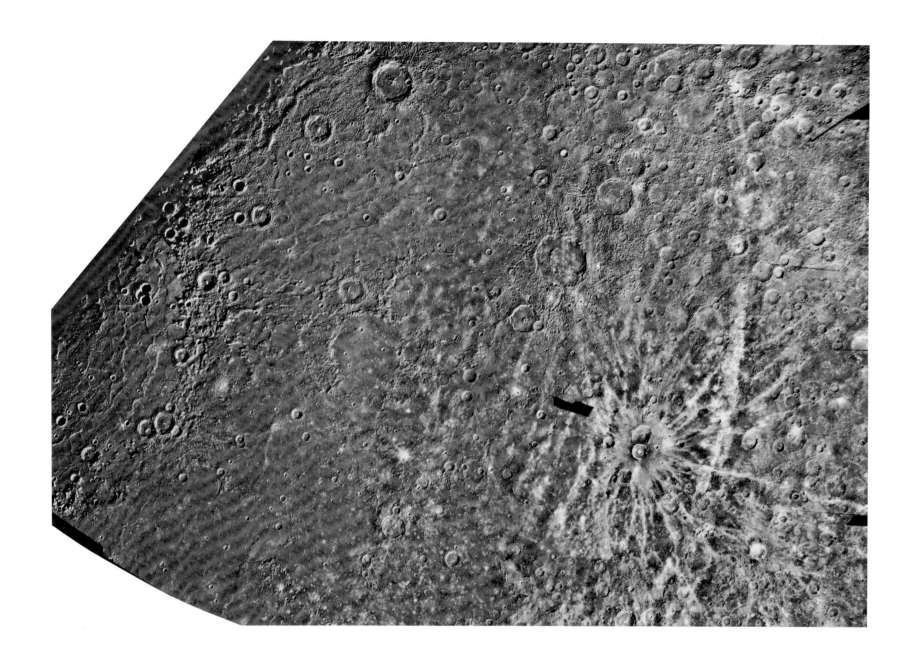

3-A   COMPUTER PHOTOMOSAIC OF THE SHAKESPEARE QUADRANGLE OF MERCURY

H-3

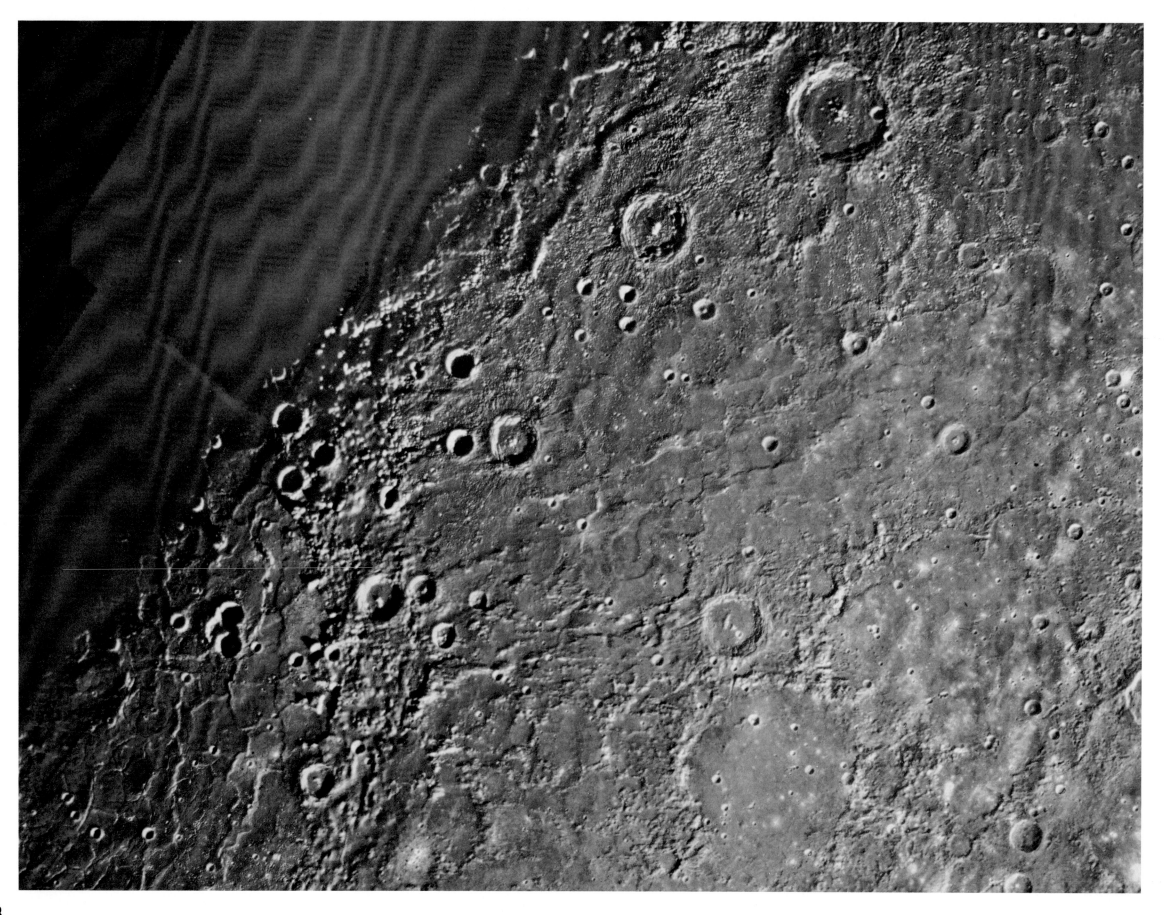

3-B   Enlarged view of the northwest region of the H-3 photomosaic

3-C   Enlarged view of the northeast region of the H-3 photomosaic

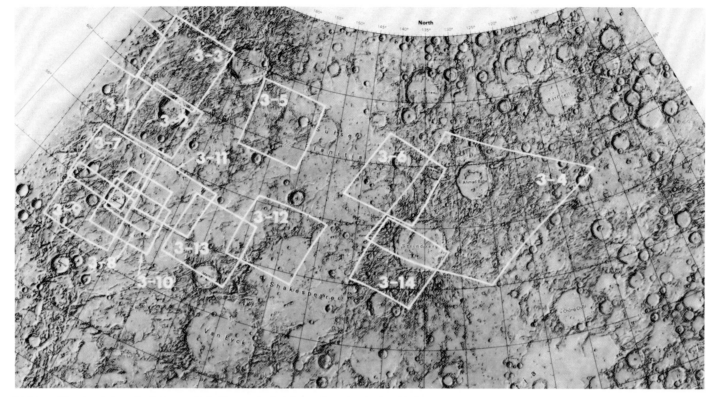

3-F1   Footprints of pictures 3-1 through 3-14 on the shaded relief map

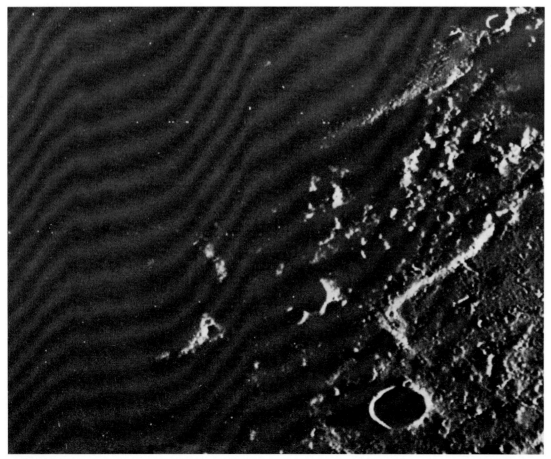

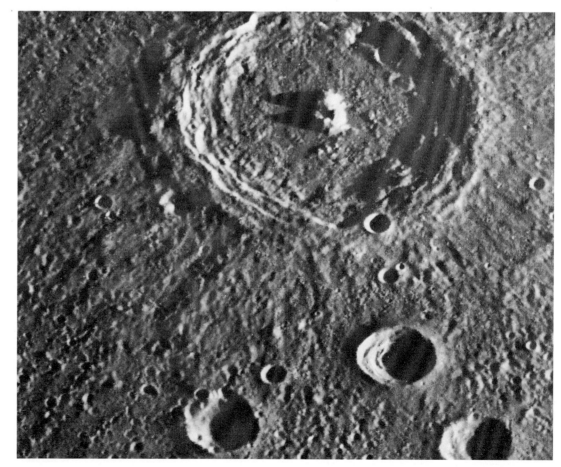

3-1   3-2

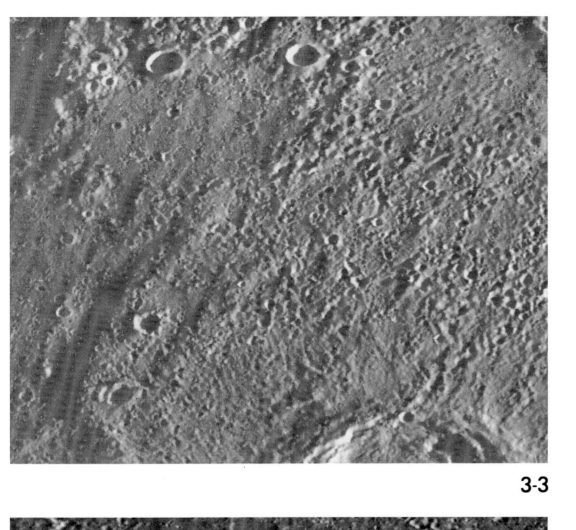

3-3

3-4

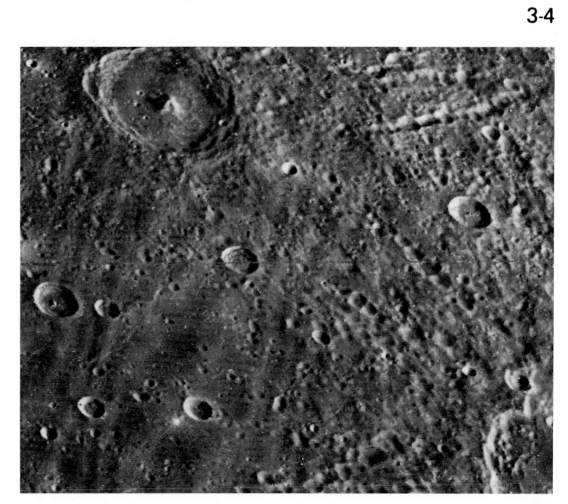

3-5

3-6

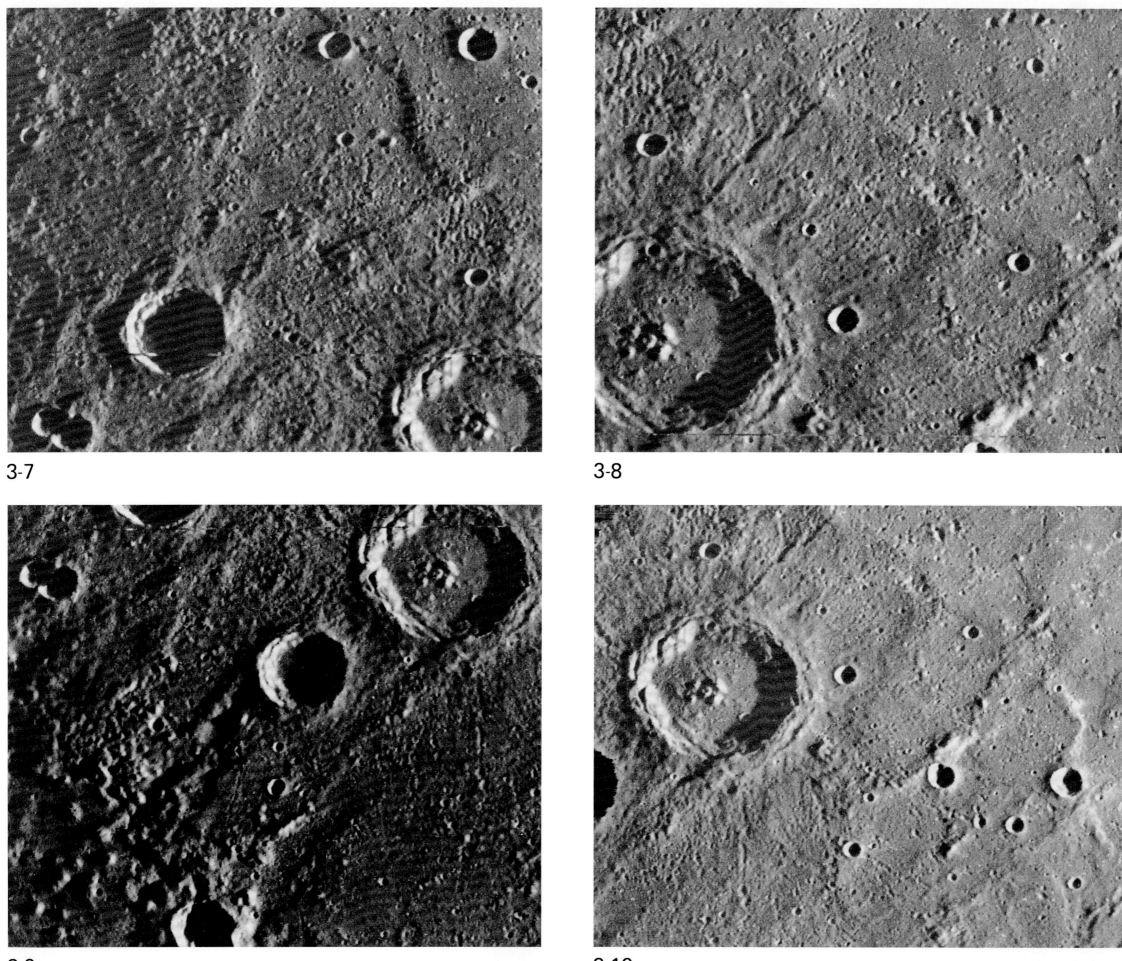

3-7

3-8

3-9

3-10

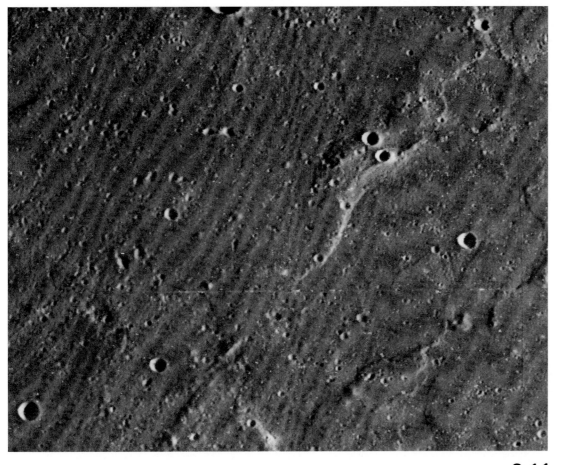

3-11

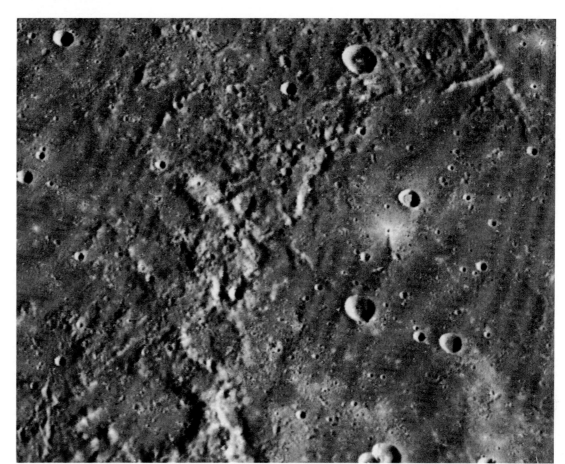

3-12

3-13

3-14

H3
47

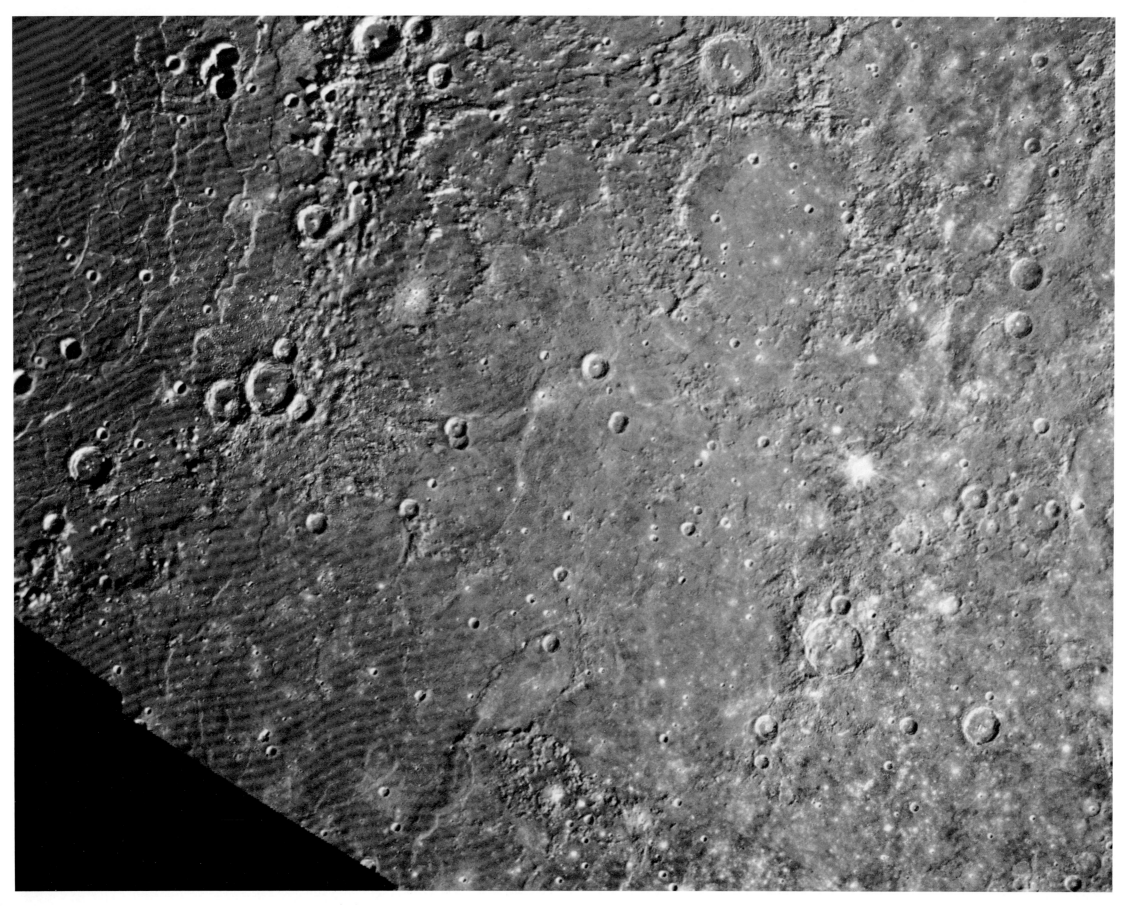

3-D   Enlarged view of the southwest region of the H-3 photomosaic

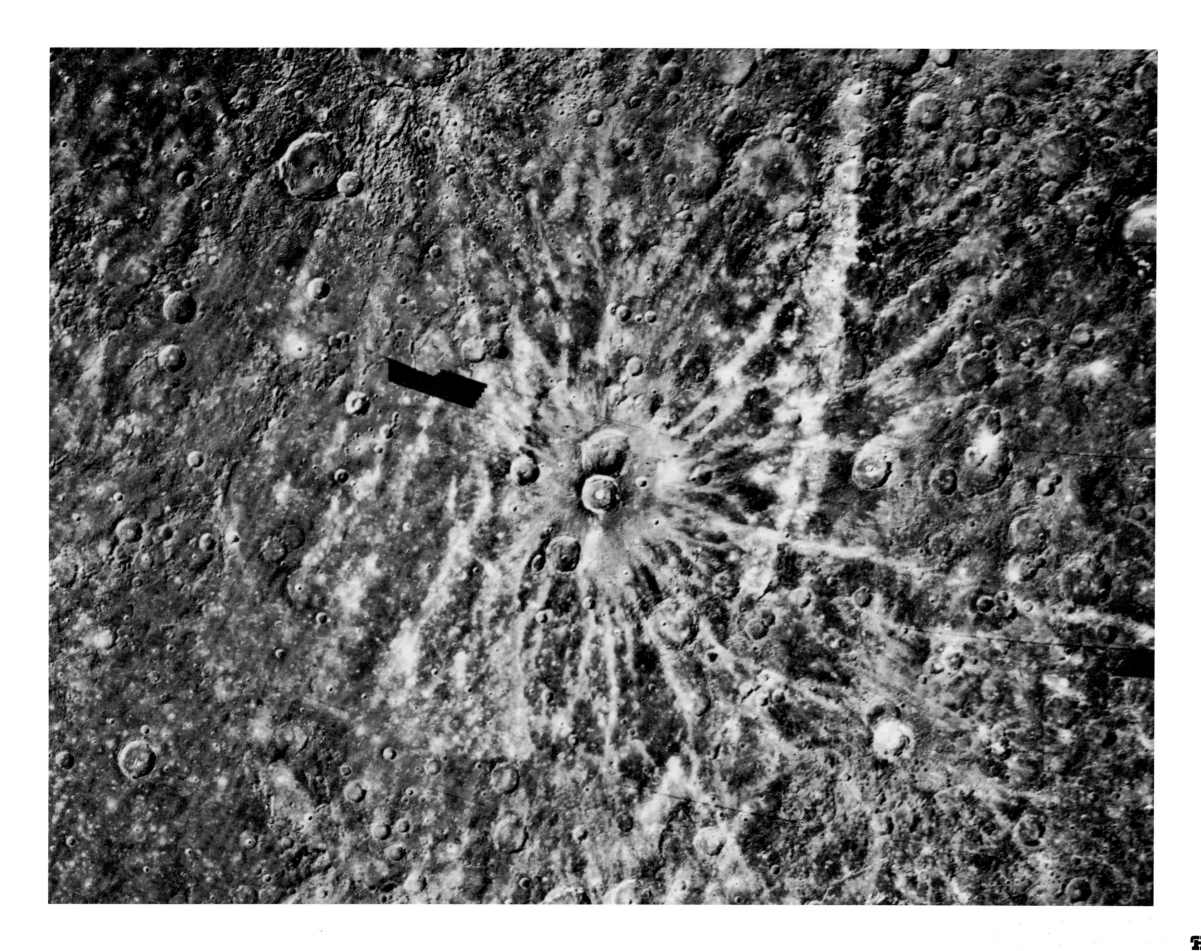

3-E   Enlarged view of the southeast region of the H-3 photomosaic

3-F2   Footprints of pictures 3-15 through 3-35 on the shaded relief map

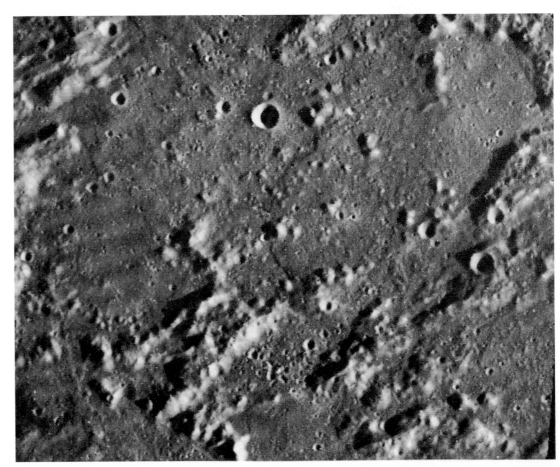

3-15   3-16

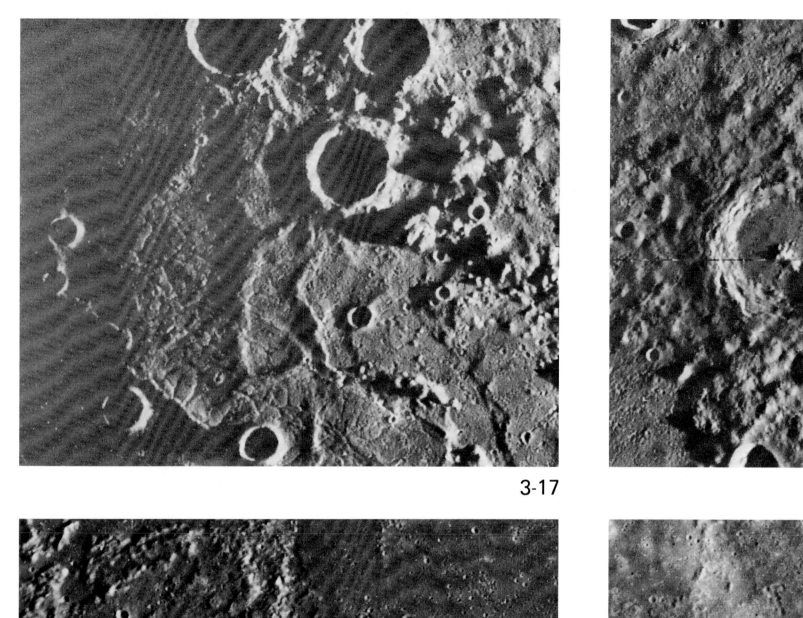

3-17

3-18

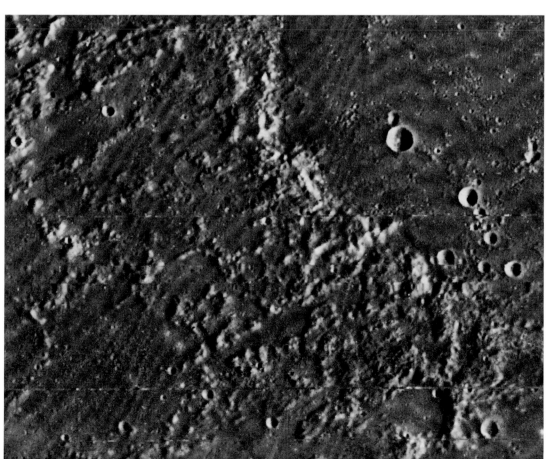

3-19

3-20

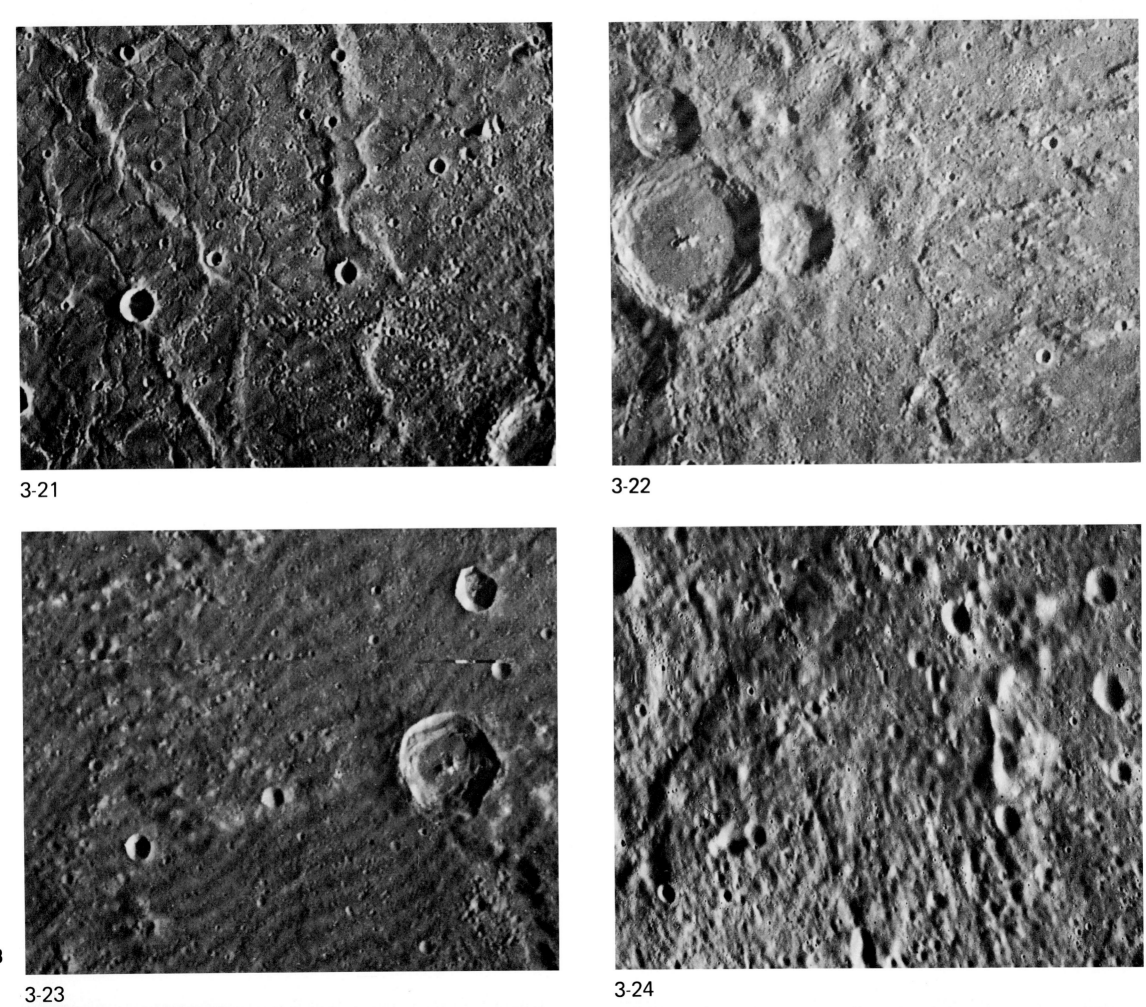

3-21

3-22

3-23

3-24

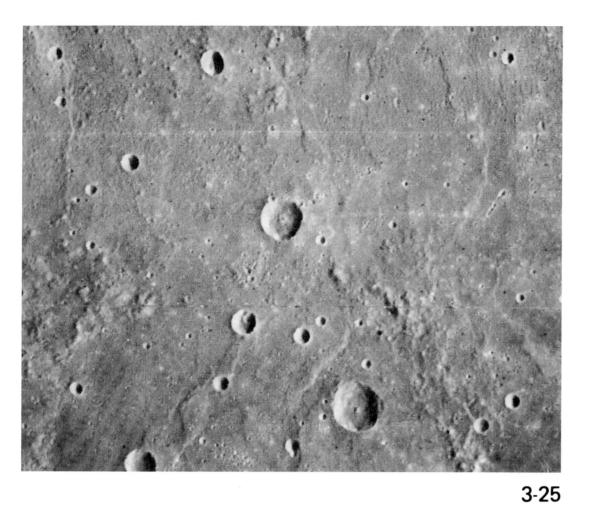

3-25

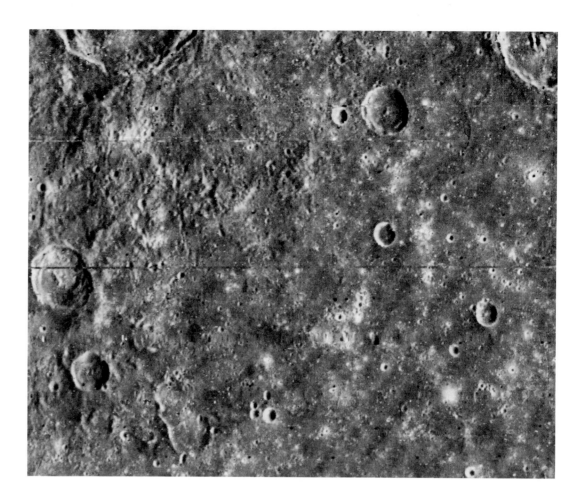

3-26

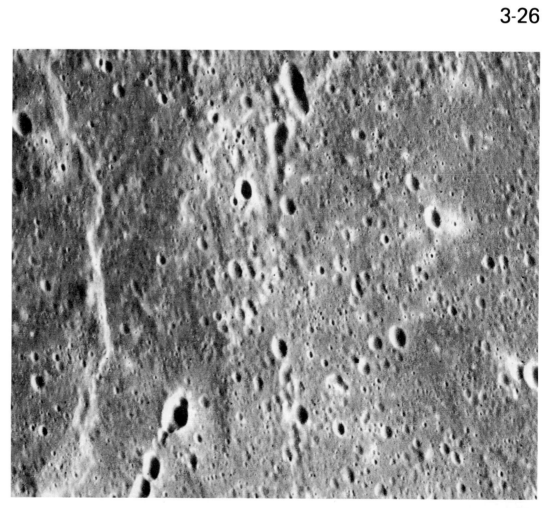

3-27

3-28

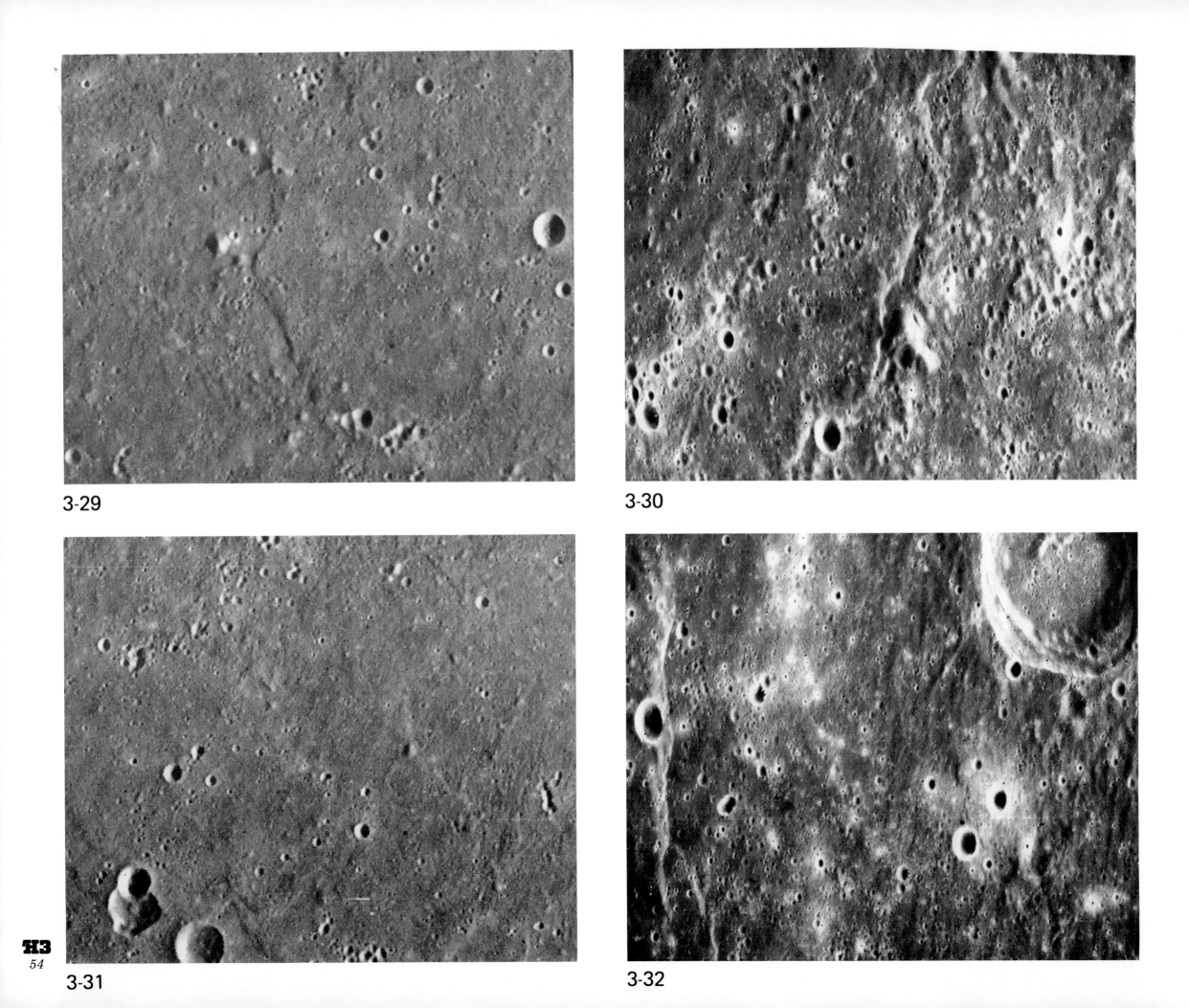

3-29

3-30

3-31

3-32

H3
54

3-33

3-34

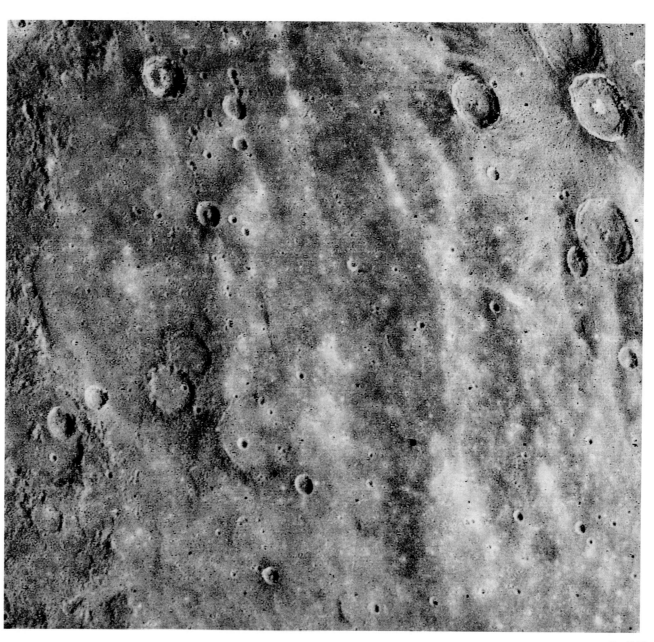

3-35

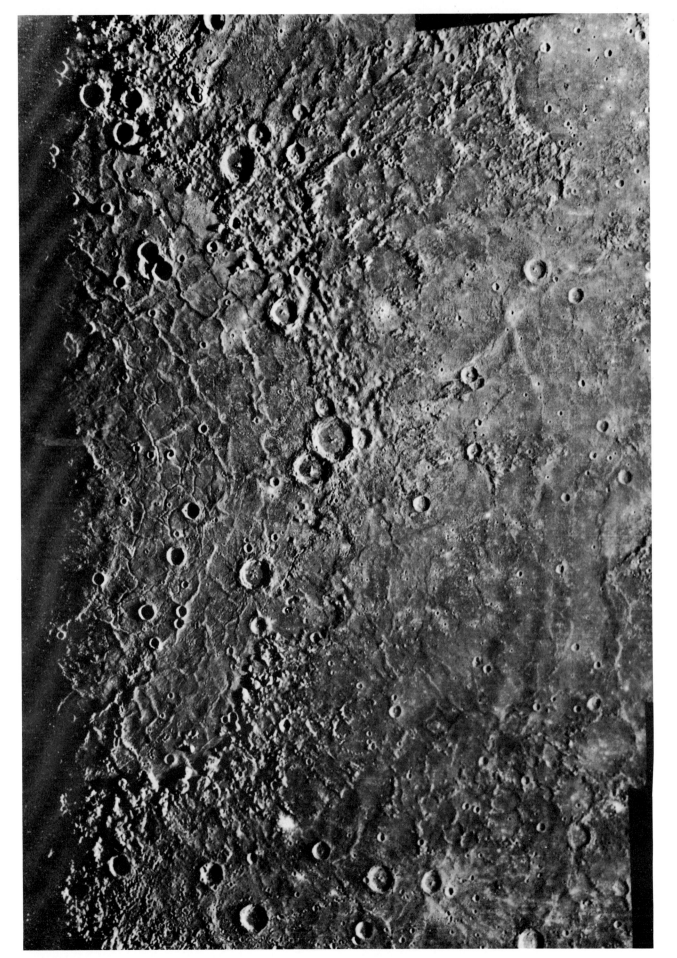

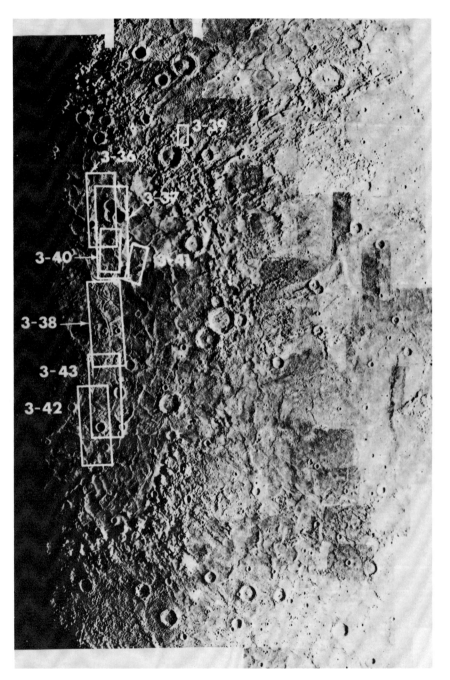

3-F3   Footprints of pictures 3-36 through 3-43 on the Caloris photomosaic.

3-F   Computer photomosaic of the Caloris basin (stereographic projection)

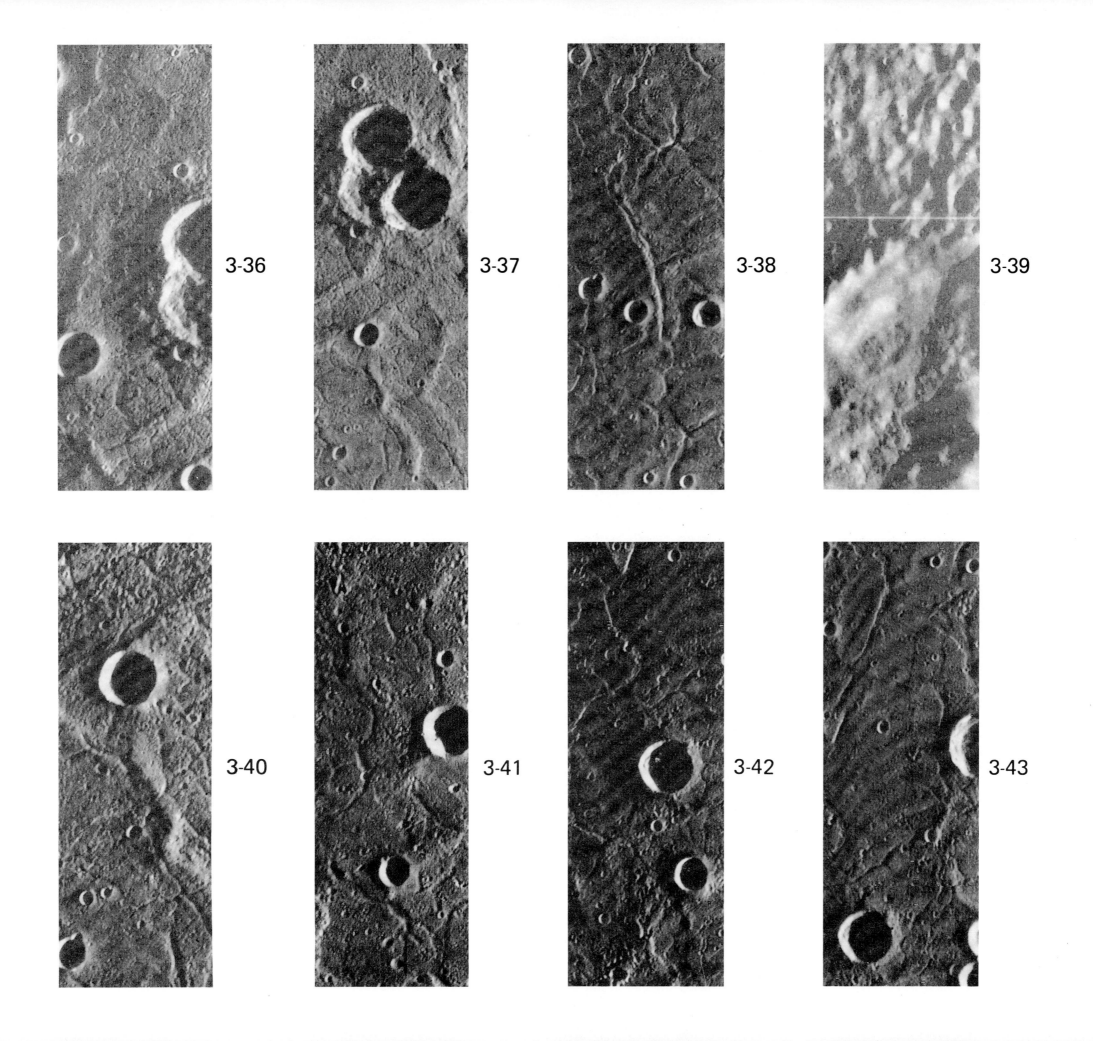

3-36

3-37

3-38

3-39

3-40

3-41

3-42

3-43

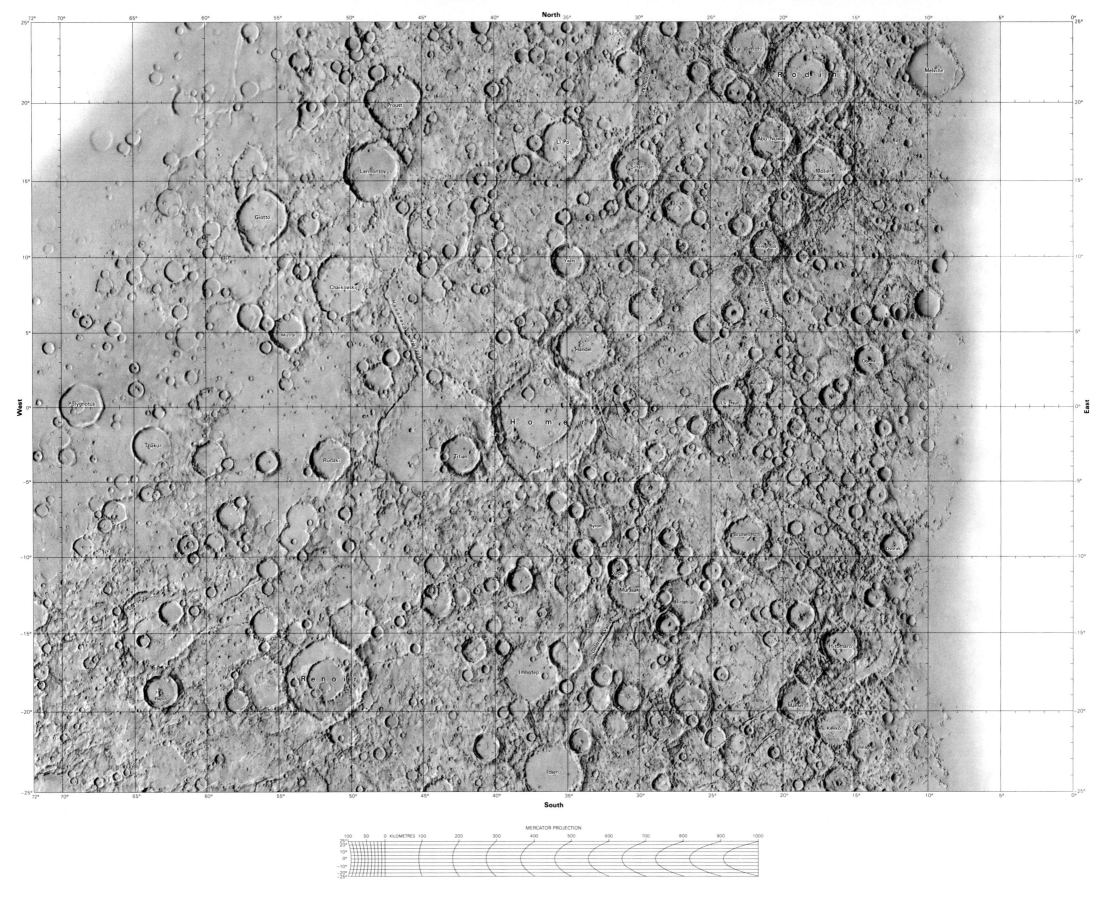

SHADED RELIEF MAP OF THE KUIPER QUADRANGLE OF MERCURY

(TRICRENA ALBEDO PROVINCE)

H-6

H 5M 0/36 R

1976

H6

58

6-A   COMPUTER PHOTOMOSAIC OF THE KUIPER QUADRANGLE OF MERCURY

H-6

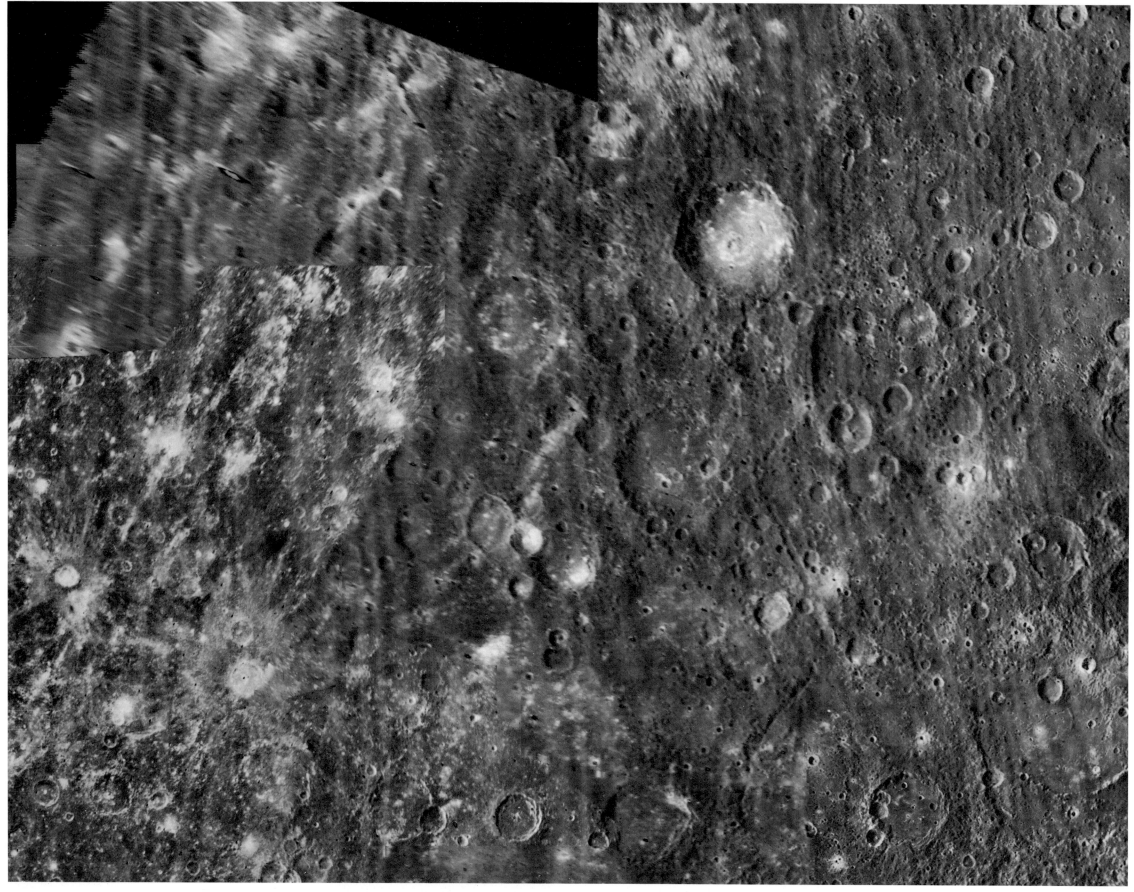

6-B   Enlarged view of the northwest region of the H-6 photomosaic

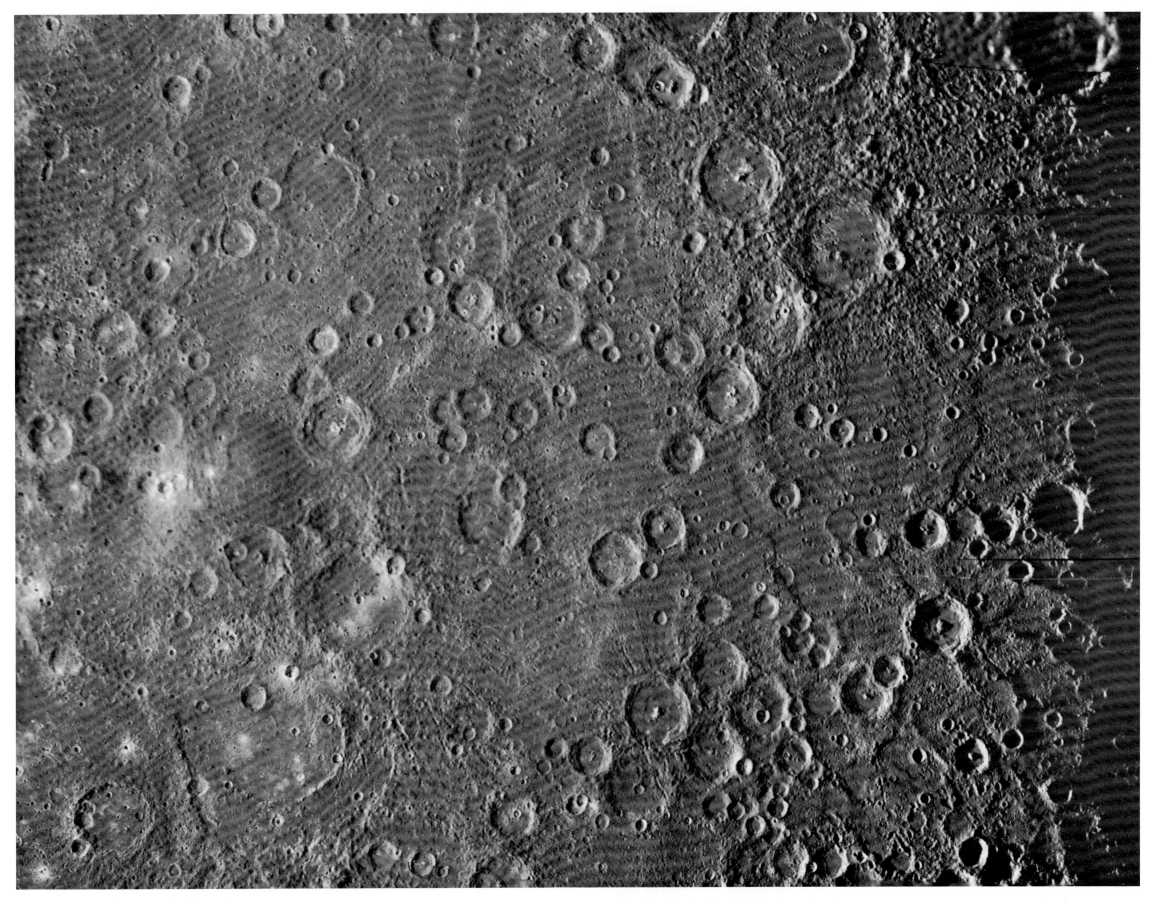

6-C   Enlarged view of the northeast region of the H-6 photomosaic

6-F1   Footprints of pictures 6-1 through 6-11 and 6-14 on the shaded relief map.

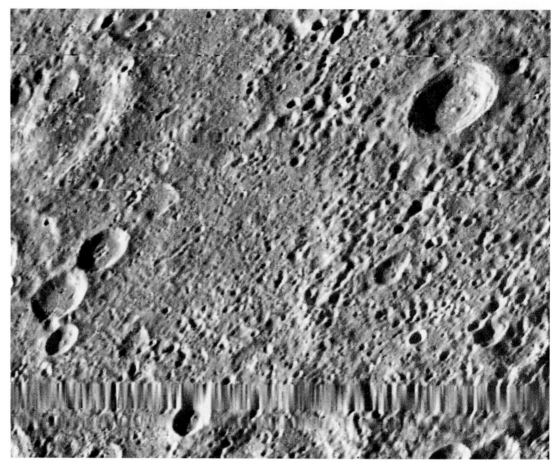

6-1

6-2

6-3

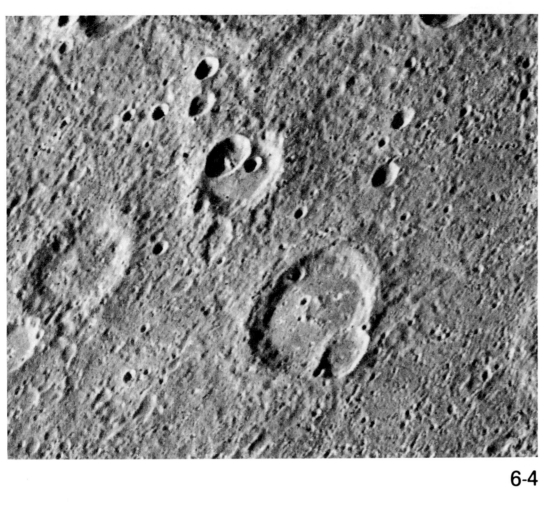

6-4

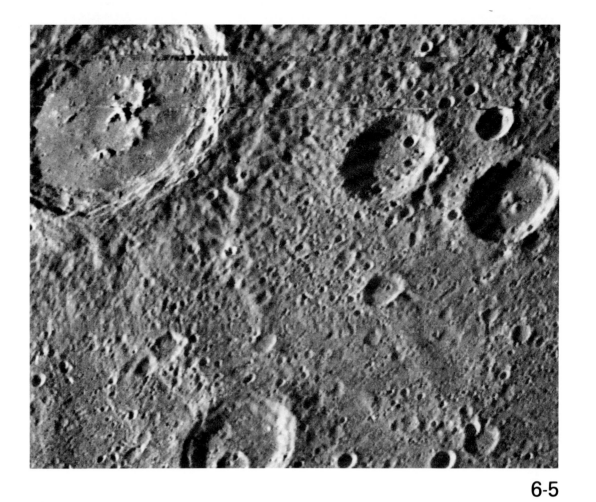

6-5

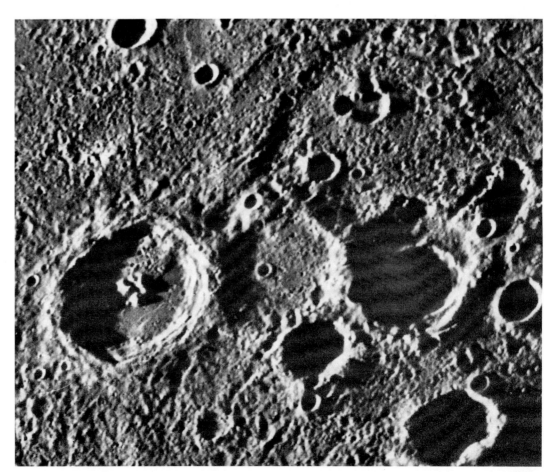

6-6

6-7

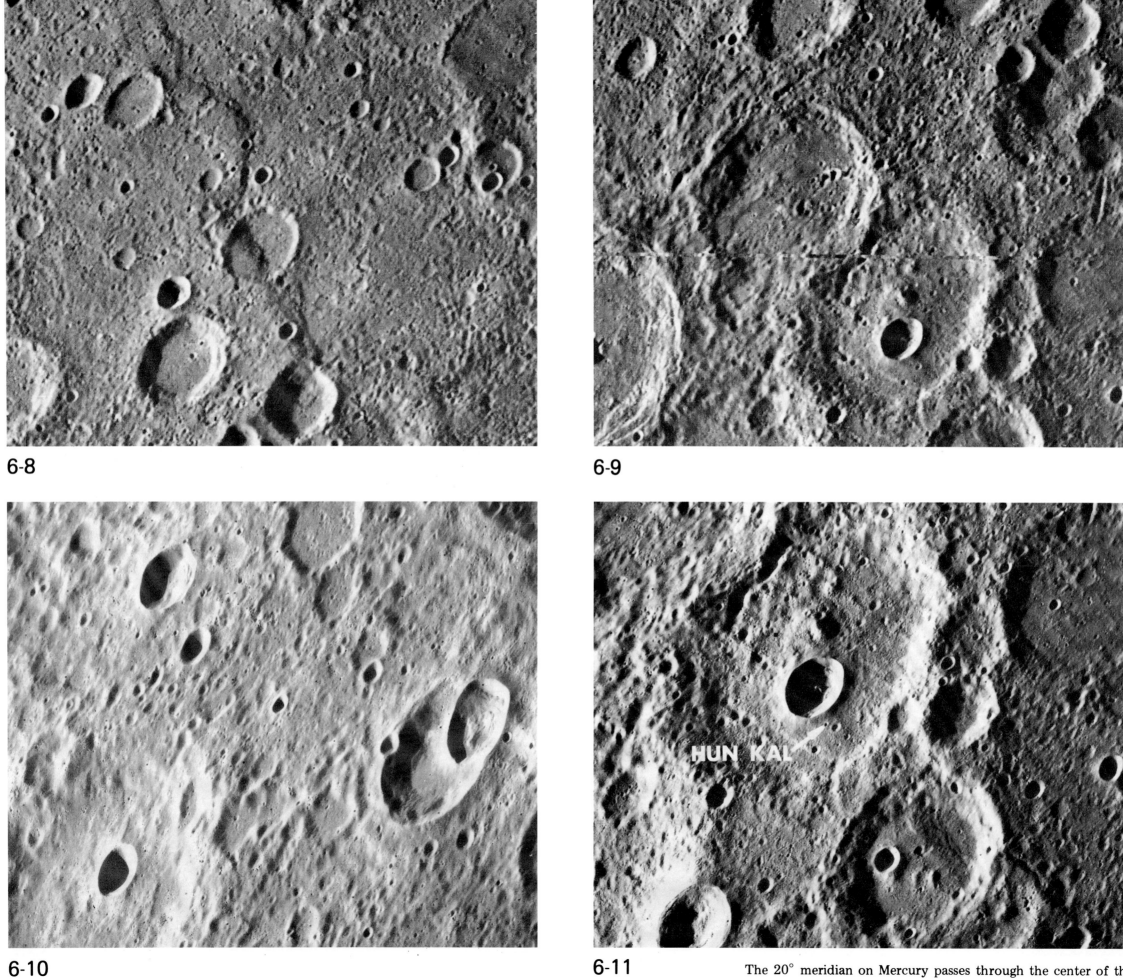

6-8

6-9

6-10

6-11

HUN KAL

H6
64

The 20° meridian on Mercury passes through the center of the crater Hun Kal

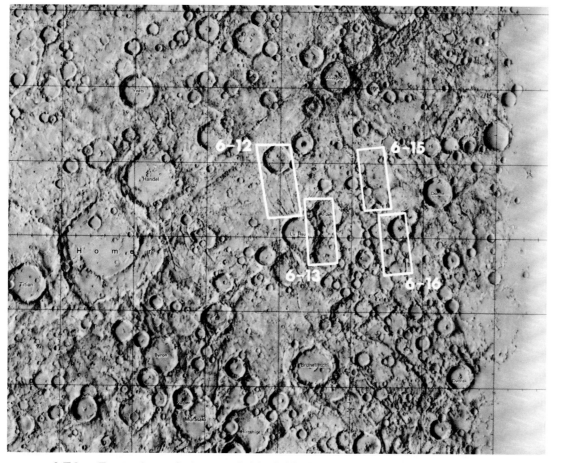

6-F2   Footprints of pictures 6-12, 6-13, 6-15, and 6-16 on the shaded relief map.

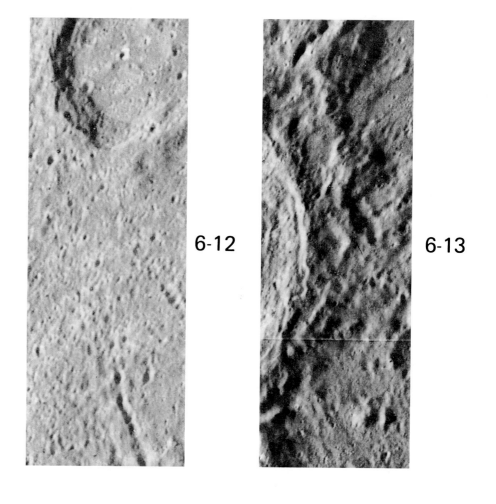

6-12

6-13

6-14

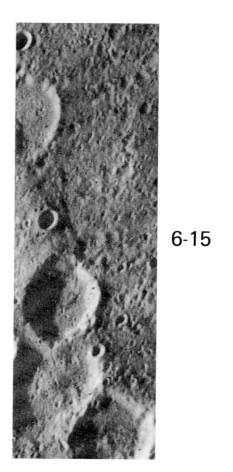

6-15

6-16

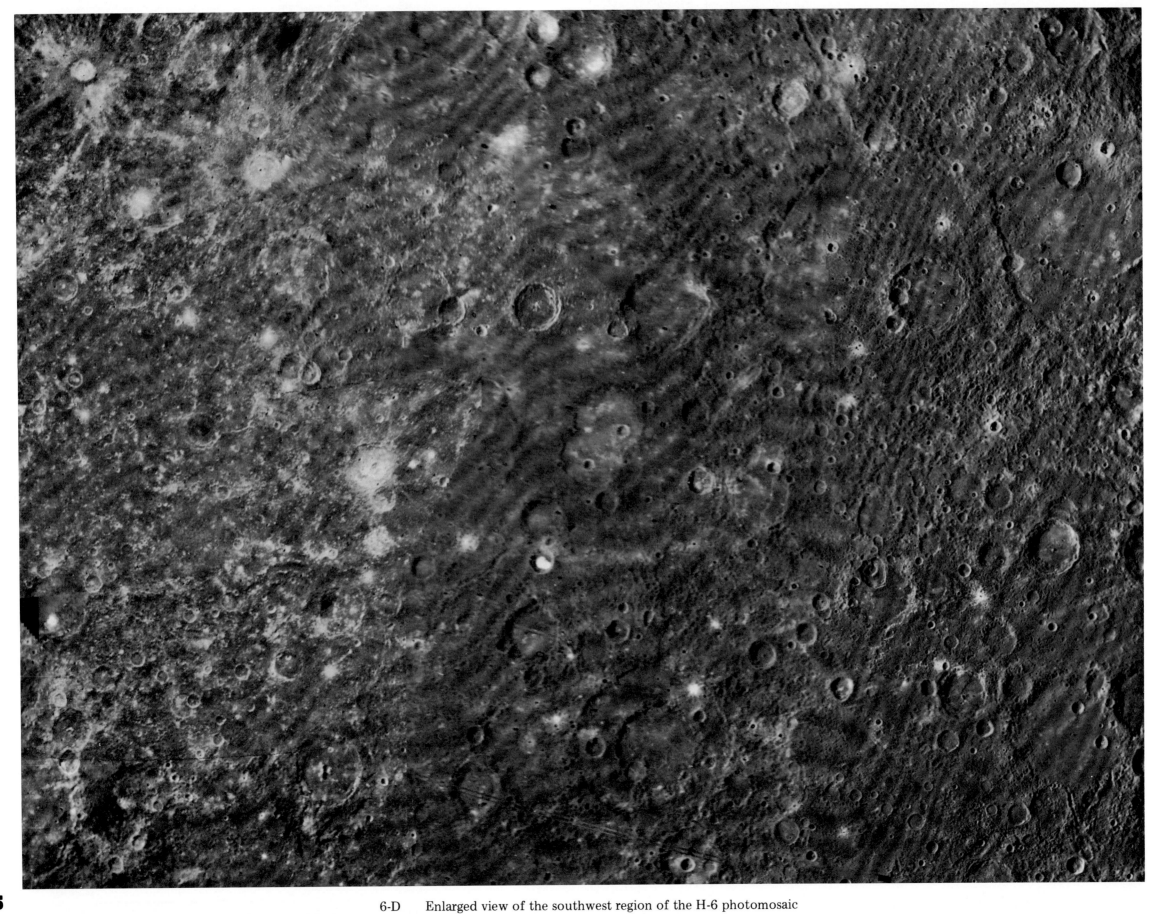

6-D   Enlarged view of the southwest region of the H-6 photomosaic

6-F3   Footprints of pictures 6-17 and stereo pairs 6-18, 6-19, and 6-20
on the shaded relief map

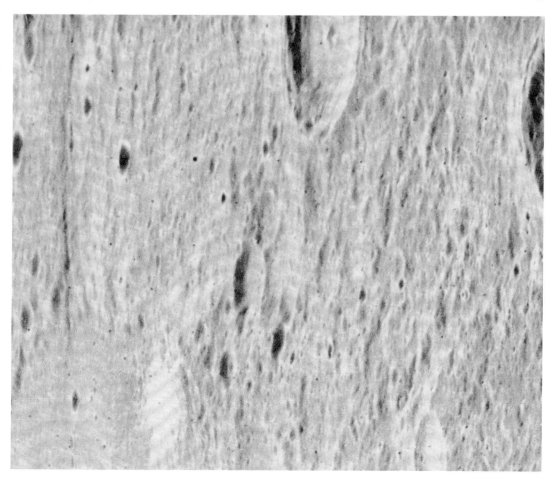

6-17

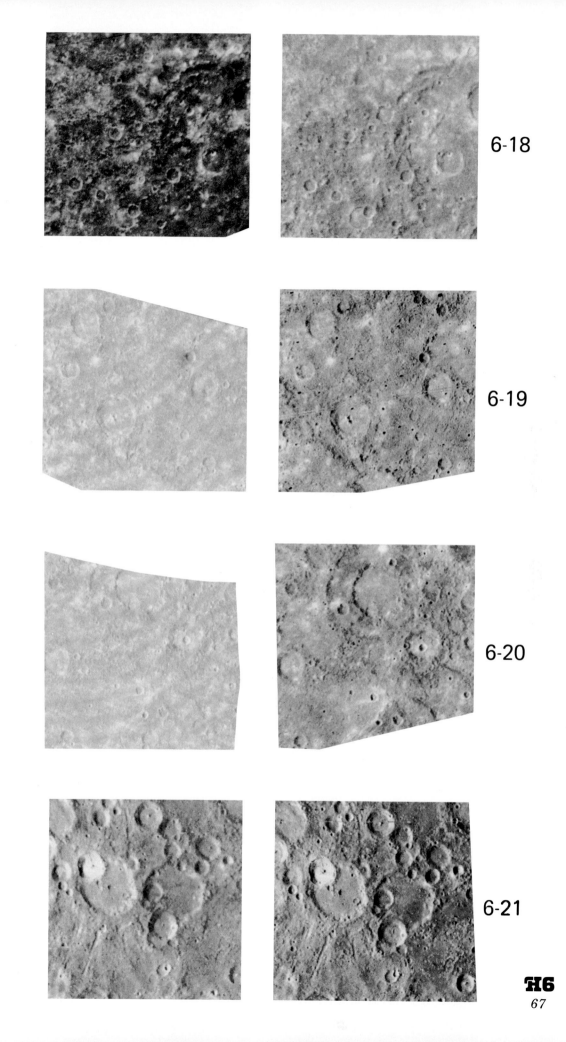

6-18

6-19

6-20

6-21

6-E   Enlarged view of the southeast region of the H-6 photomosaic

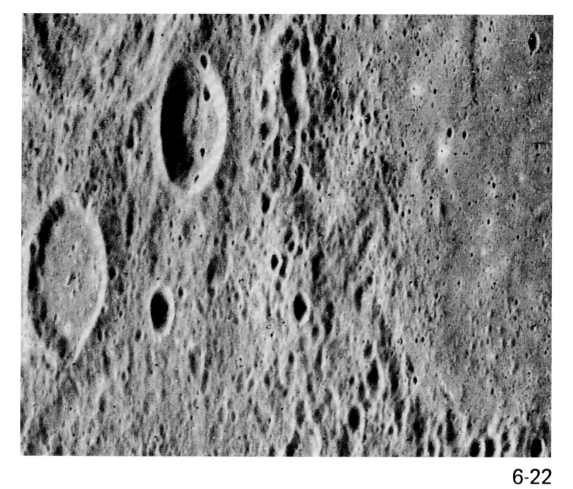

6-22

6-F4   Footprints of pictures 6-21 through 6-29 on the shaded relief map.

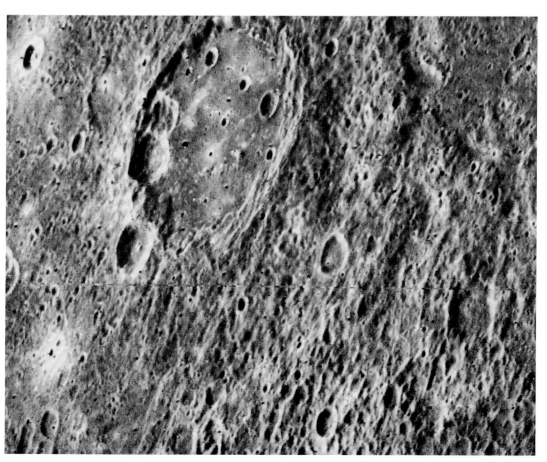

6-23

6-24

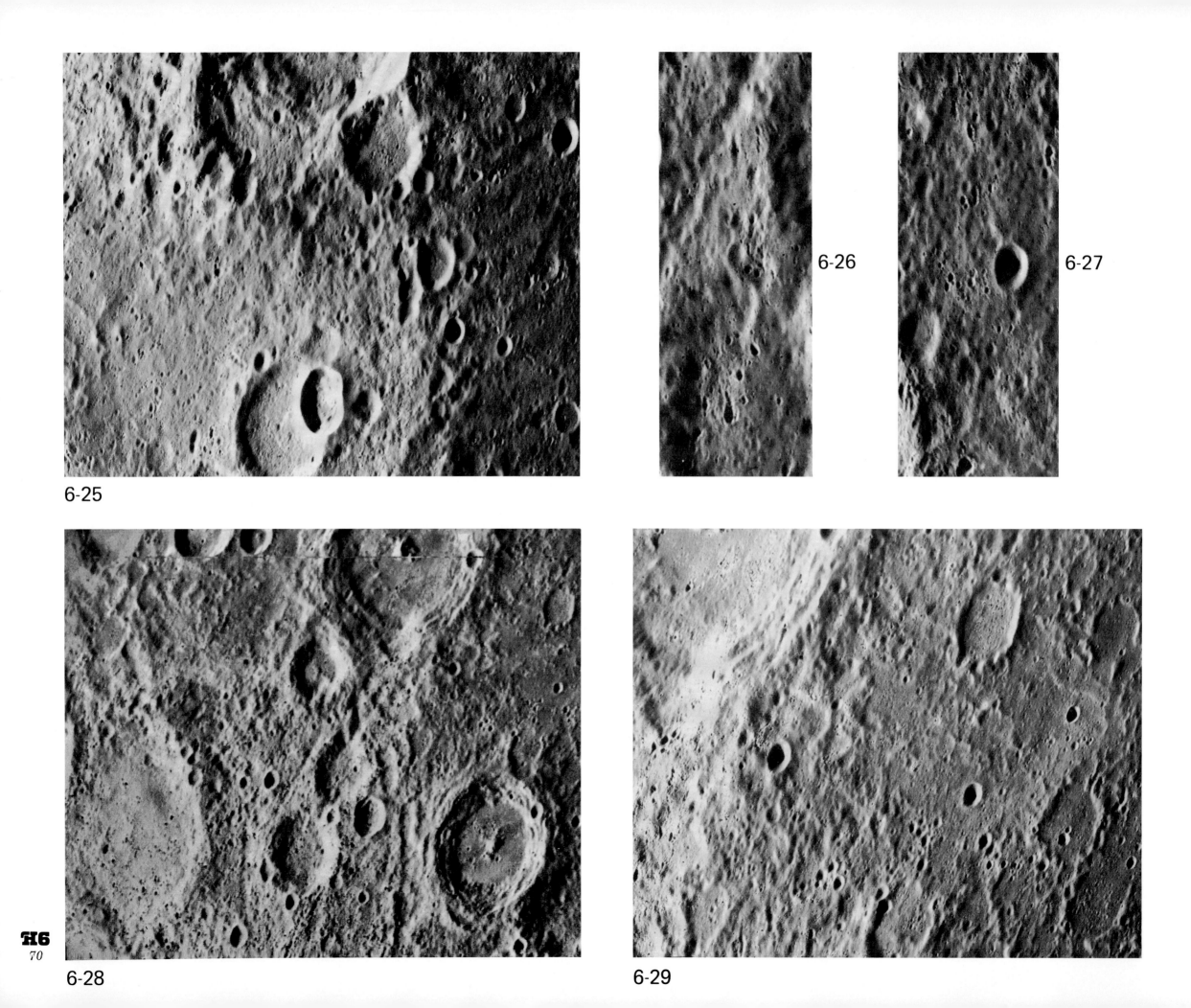

6-25

6-26

6-27

6-28

6-29

H6
70

6-30

6-31

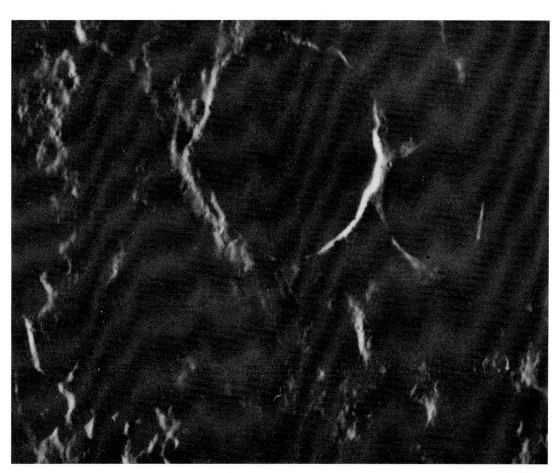

6-F5   Footprints of pictures 6-30 through 6-40 on the shaded relief map

6-32

6-33

6-34

6-35

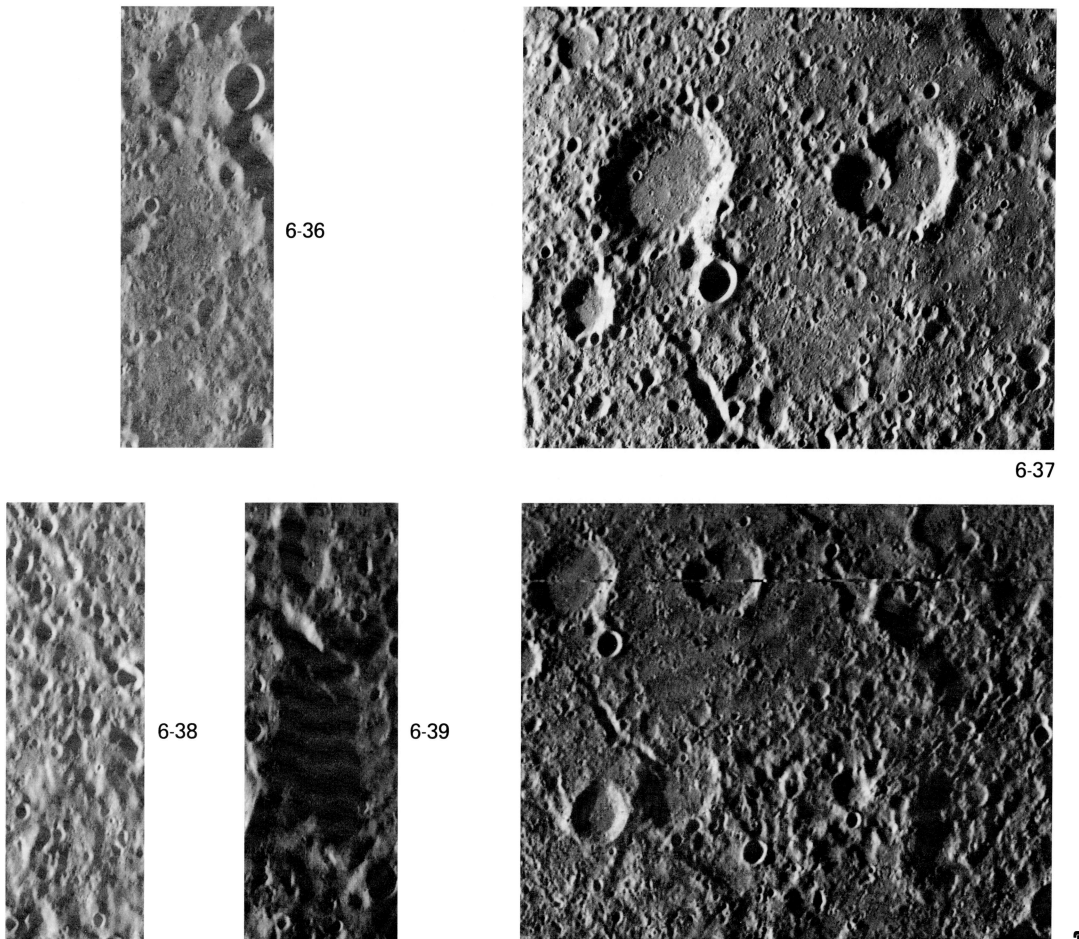

6-36

6-37

6-38

6-39

6-40

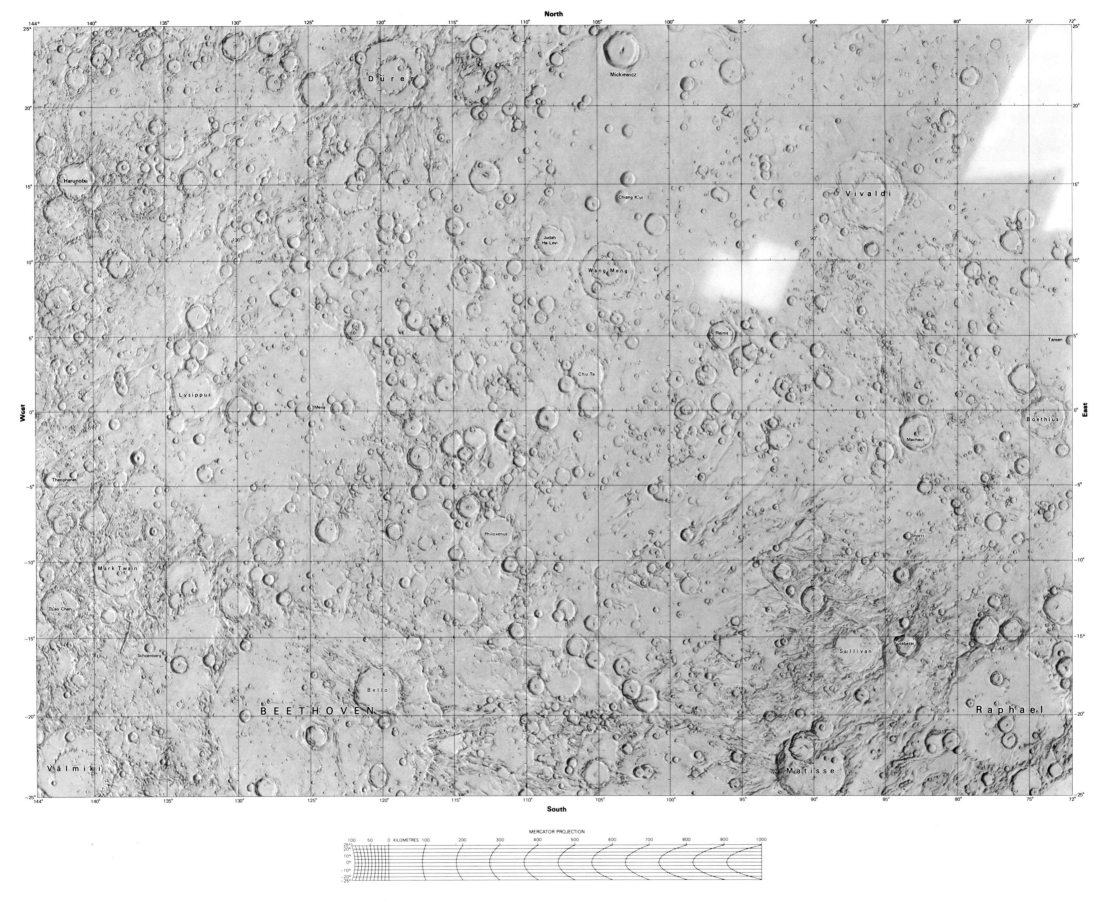

North

South

West · East

Dürer · Mickiewicz · Vivaldi · Harunobu · Chiang K'ui · Judah Ha-Levi · Wang Meng · Rajnis · Tansen · Chu Ta · Lysippus · Mena · Boethius · Machaut · Theophanes · Sher-Gil · Philoxenus · Mark Twain · Ts'ao Chan · Schoenberg · Sullivan · Surikov · Bello · BEETHOVEN · Raphael · Vālmīki · Matisse

MERCATOR PROJECTION

100 50 0 KILOMETRES 100 200 300 400 500 600 700 800 900 1000

H7

74

SHADED RELIEF MAP OF THE BEETHOVEN QUADRANGLE OF MERCURY
(SOLITUDO LYCAONIS ALBEDO PROVINCE)
H-7
H 5M 0/108 R
1976

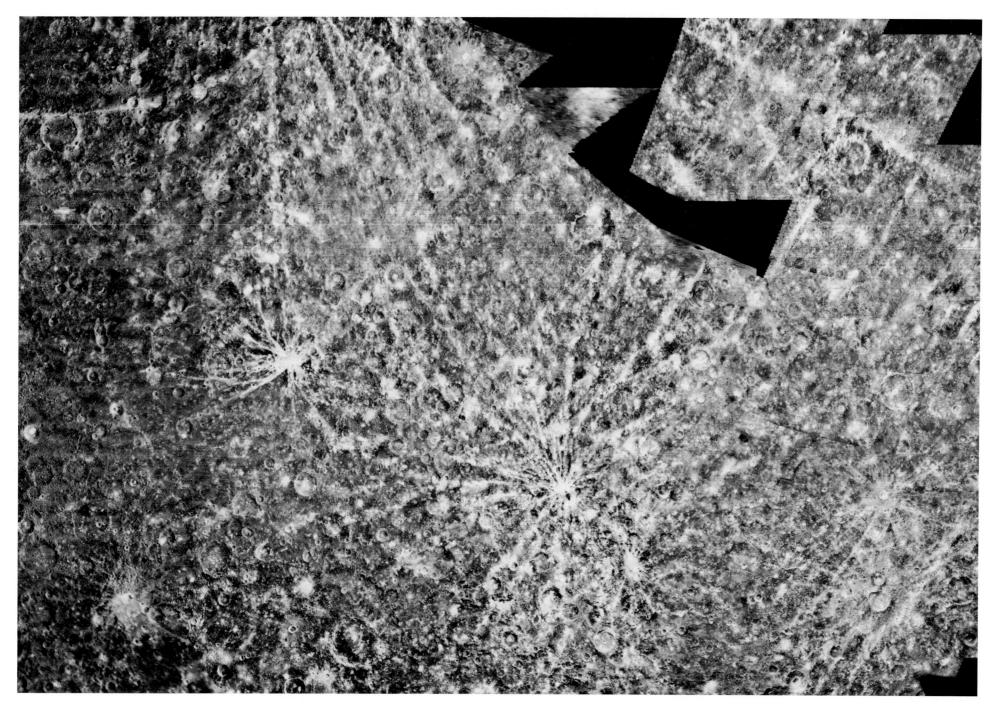

7-A   COMPUTER PHOTOMOSAIC OF THE BEETHOVEN QUADRANGLE OF MERCURY

H-7

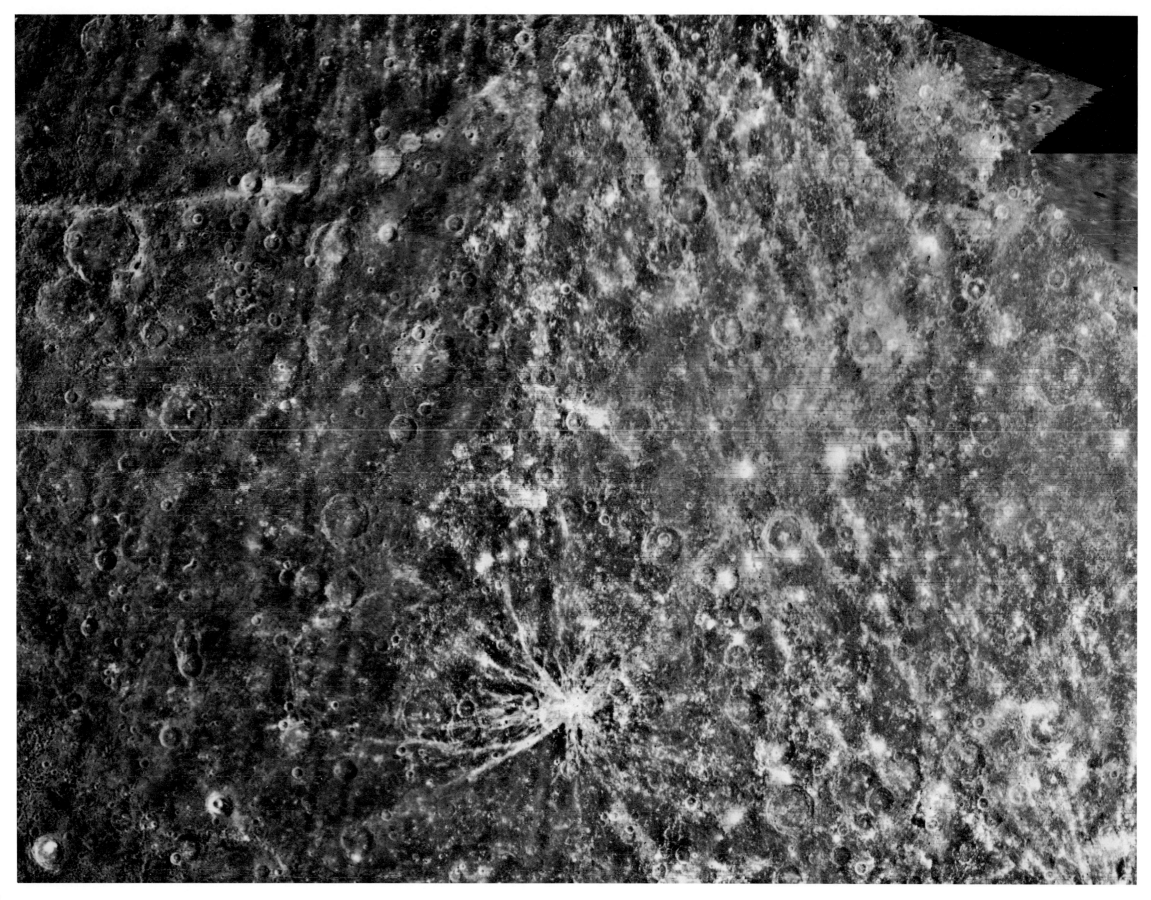

7-B   Enlarged view of the northwest region of the H-7 photomosaic

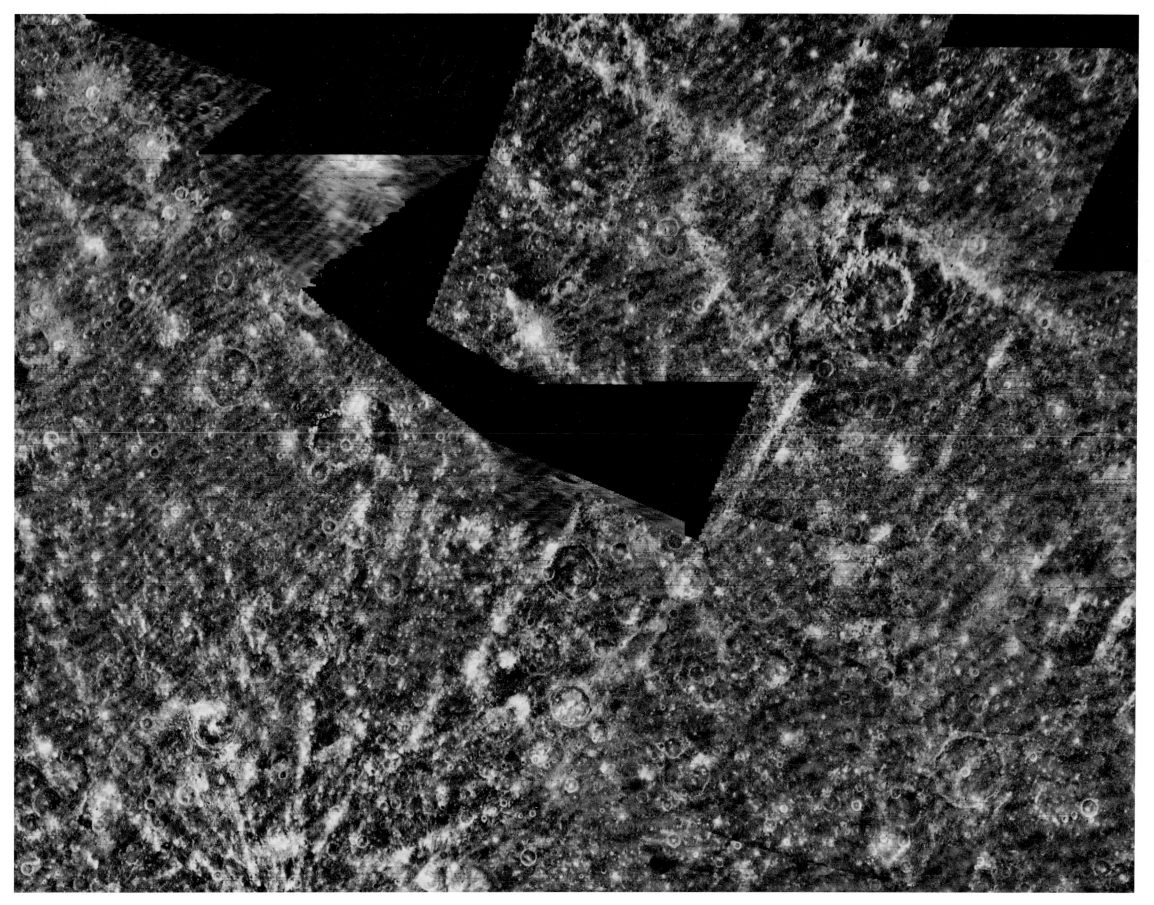

7-C   Enlarged view of the northeast region of the H-7 photomosaic

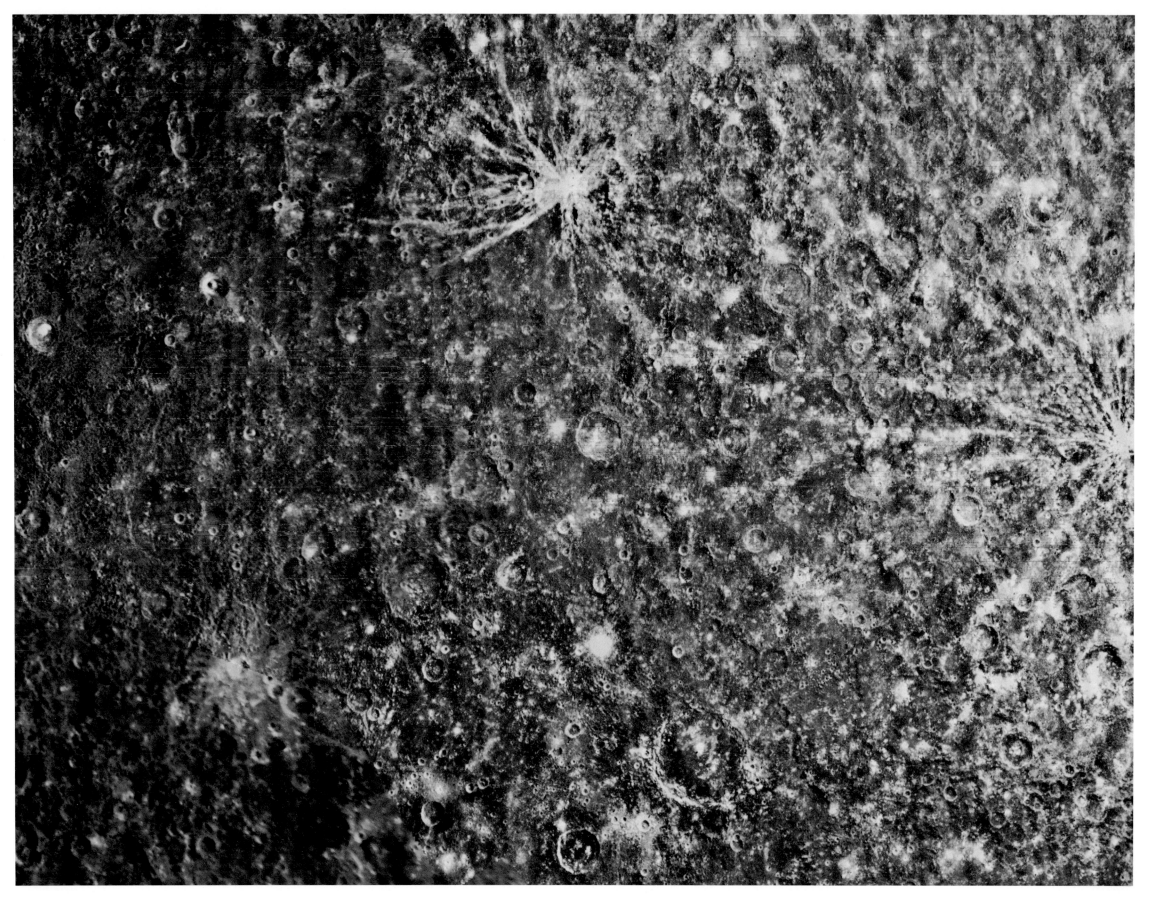

7-D   Enlarged view of the southwest region of the H-7 photomosaic

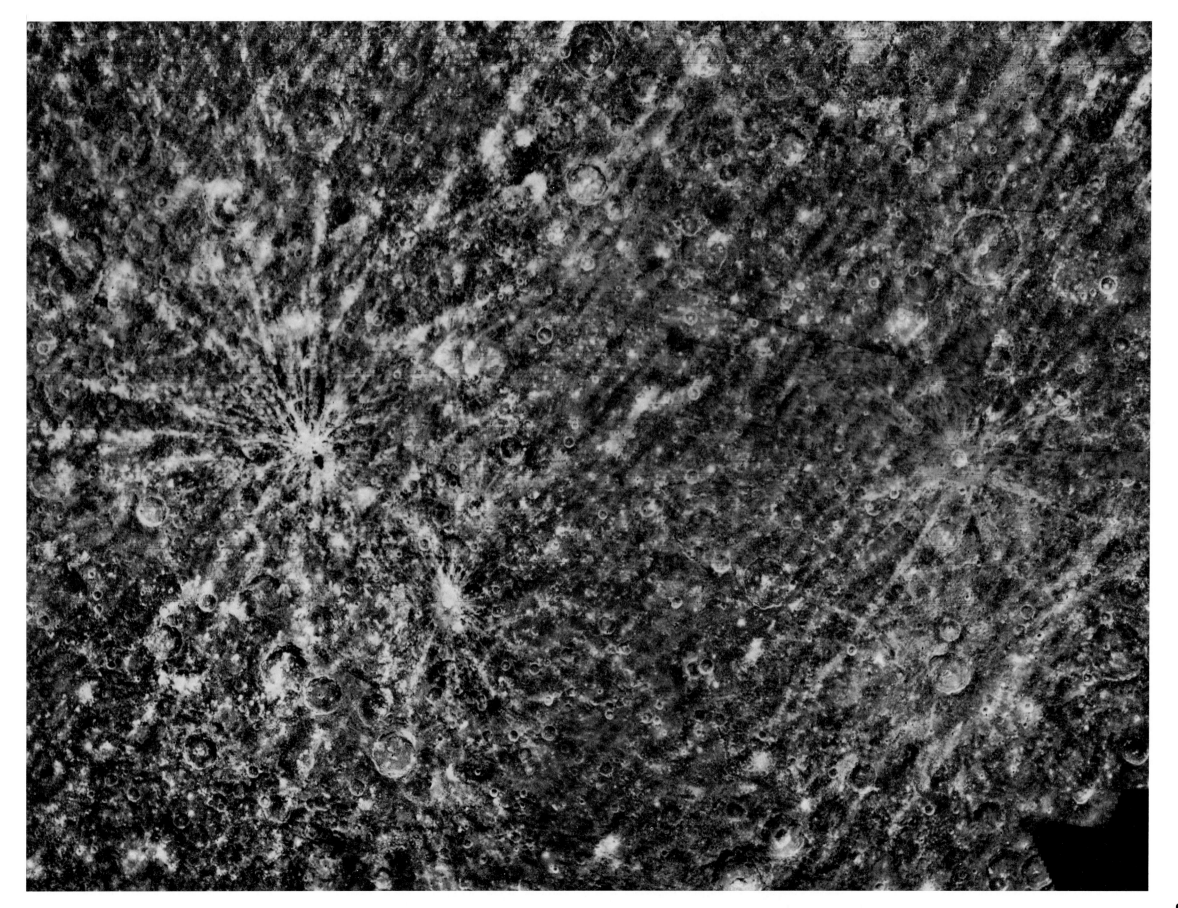

7-E   Enlarged view of the southeast region of the H-7 photomosaic

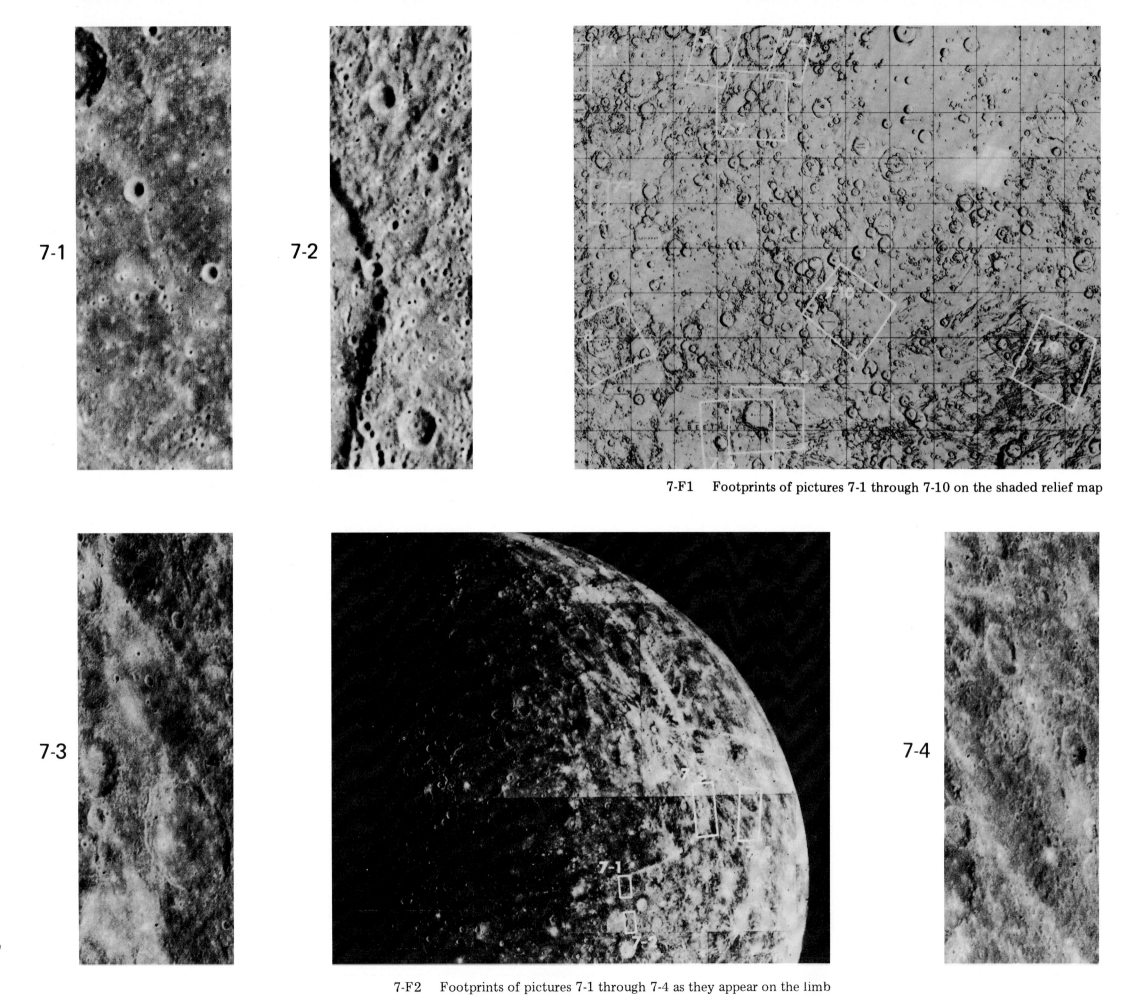

7-1

7-2

7-F1   Footprints of pictures 7-1 through 7-10 on the shaded relief map

7-3

7-4

H7
80

7-F2   Footprints of pictures 7-1 through 7-4 as they appear on the limb

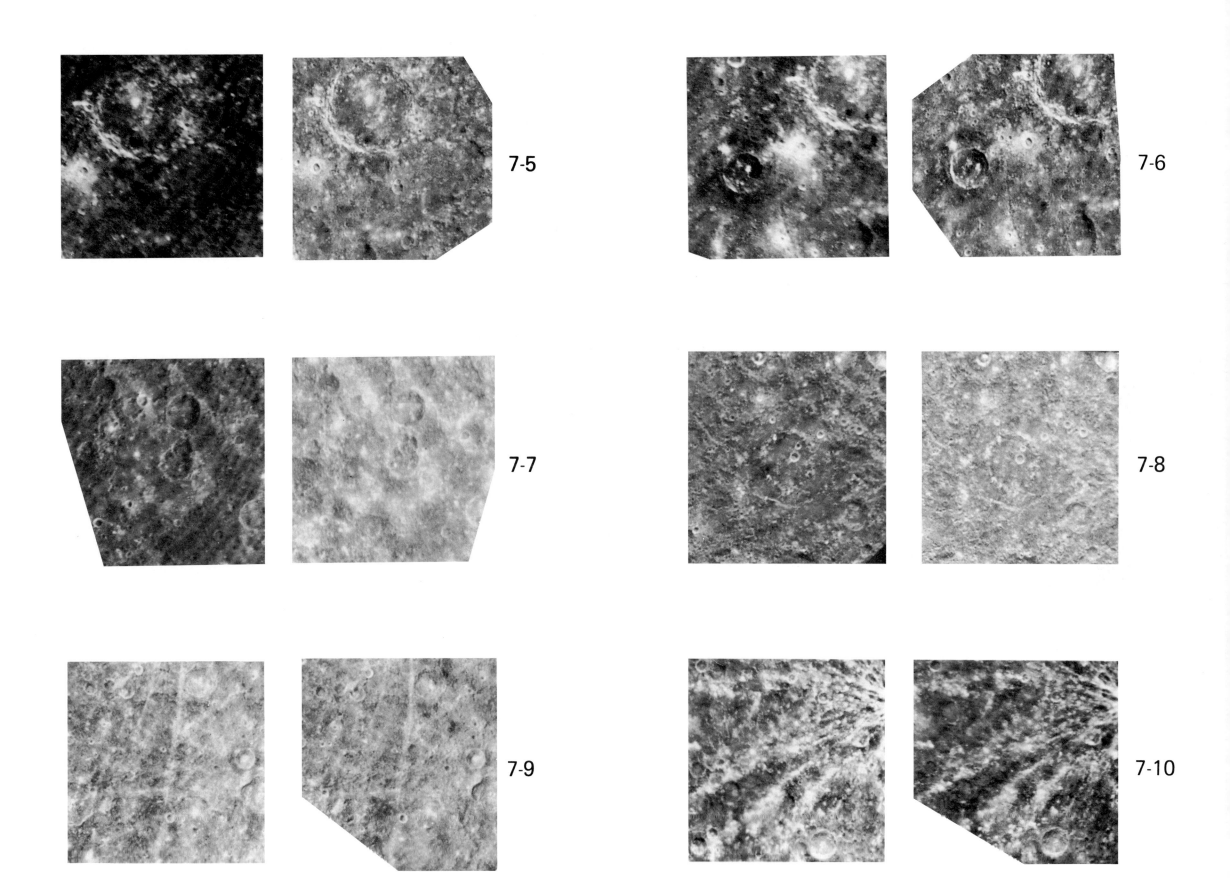

7-5

7-6

7-7

7-8

7-9

7-10

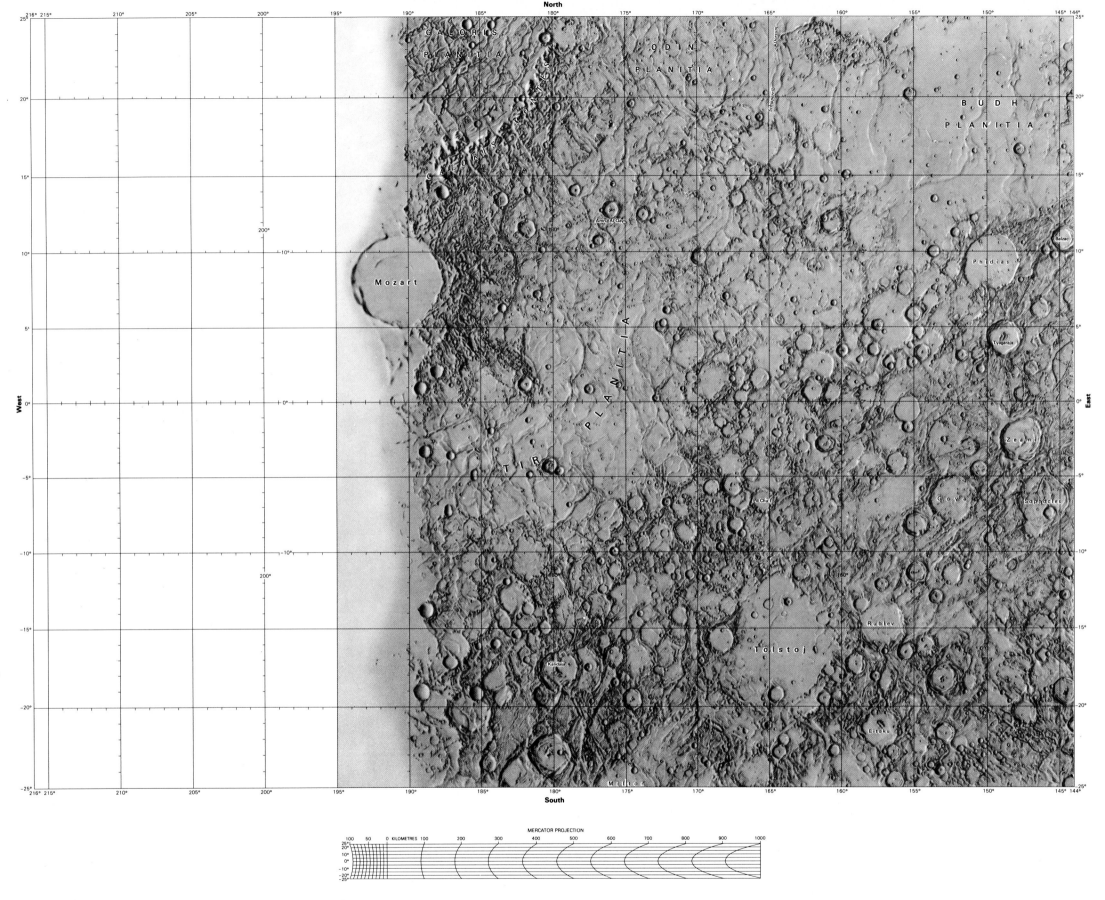

MERCATOR PROJECTION

SHADED RELIEF MAP OF THE TOLSTOJ QUADRANGLE OF MERCURY
(PHAETHONTIAS ALBEDO PROVINCE)
H-8
H 5M 0/180 R
1976

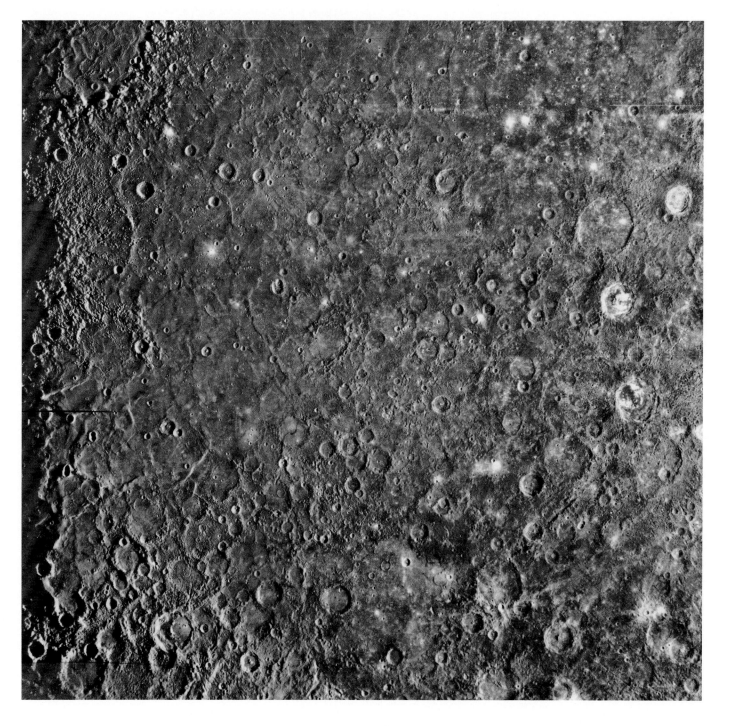

8-A   COMPUTER PHOTOMOSAIC OF THE TOLSTOJ QUADRANGLE OF MERCURY
H-8

8-B   Enlarged view of the northwest region of the H-8 photomosaic

8-D   Enlarged view of the southwest region of the H-8 photomosaic

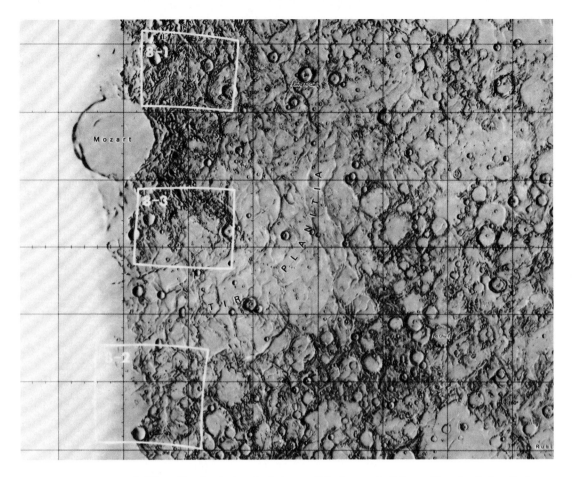

8-F1   Footprints of pictures 8-1 through 8-3 on the shaded relief map

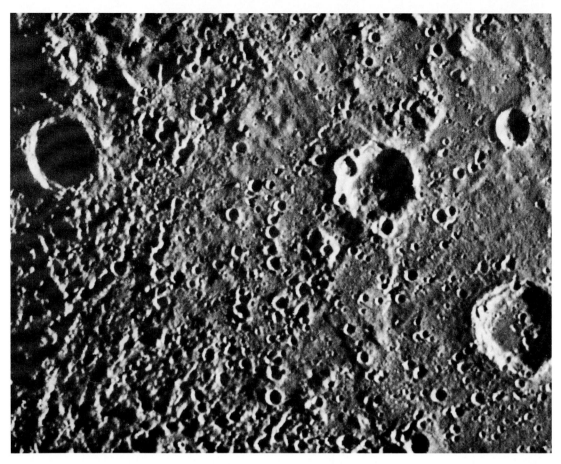

8-1

8-2

8-3

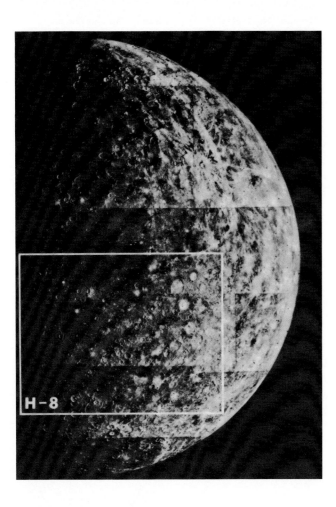

8-F2   Footprint of the H-8 quadrangle plotted on a mosaic compiled from pictures taken by the departing spacecraft within 2 hours after closest approach.

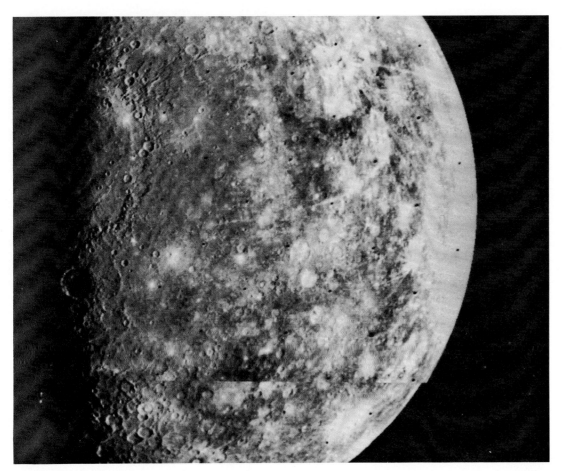

8-5

Pictures 8-4 and 8-5 were taken by the departing spacecraft 12 hours after the pictures compiling the mosaic shown in 8-F2. Additional topography, in particular the crater Mozart, is shown as it emerges from the morning terminator.

8-4

8-C   Enlarged view of the northeast region of the H-8 photomosaic

8-E   Enlarged view of the southeast region of the H-8 photomosaic

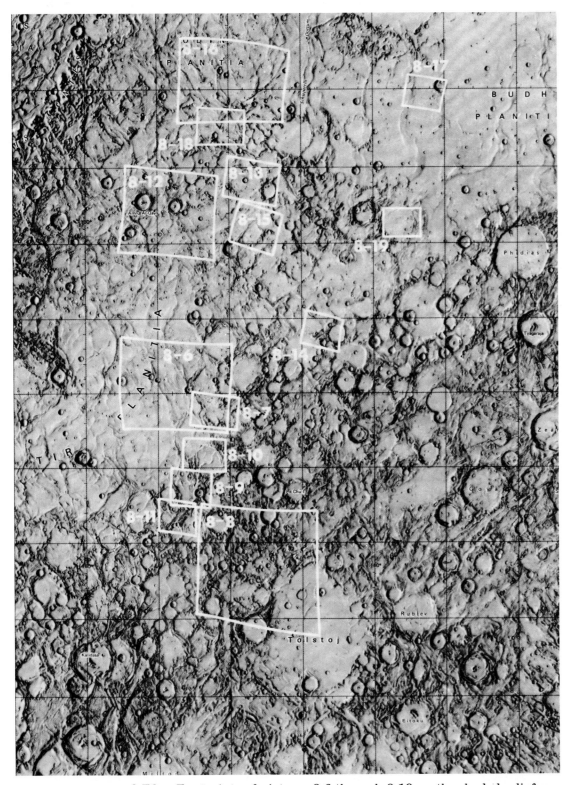

8-F3   Footprints of pictures 8-6 through 8-19 on the shaded relief map

8-6

8-7

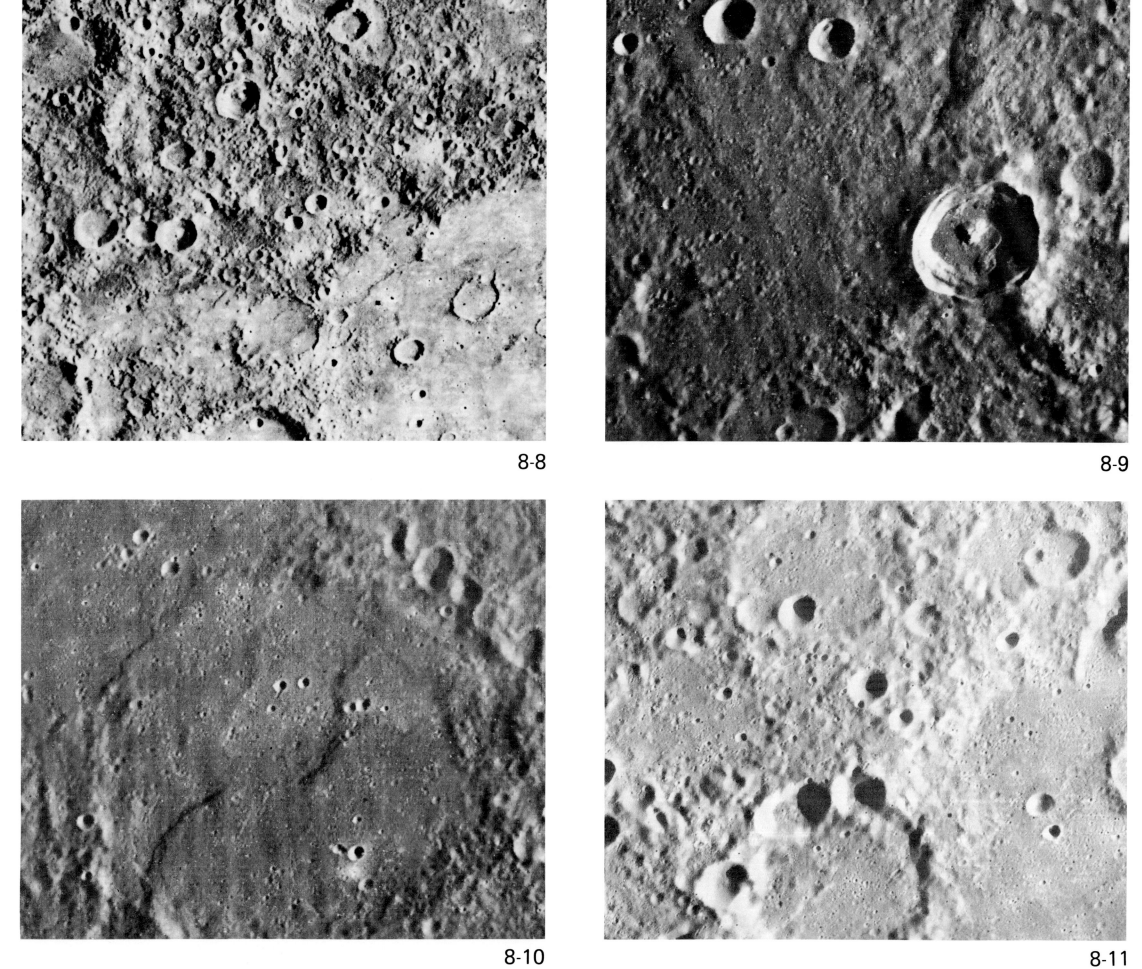

8-8

8-9

8-10

8-11

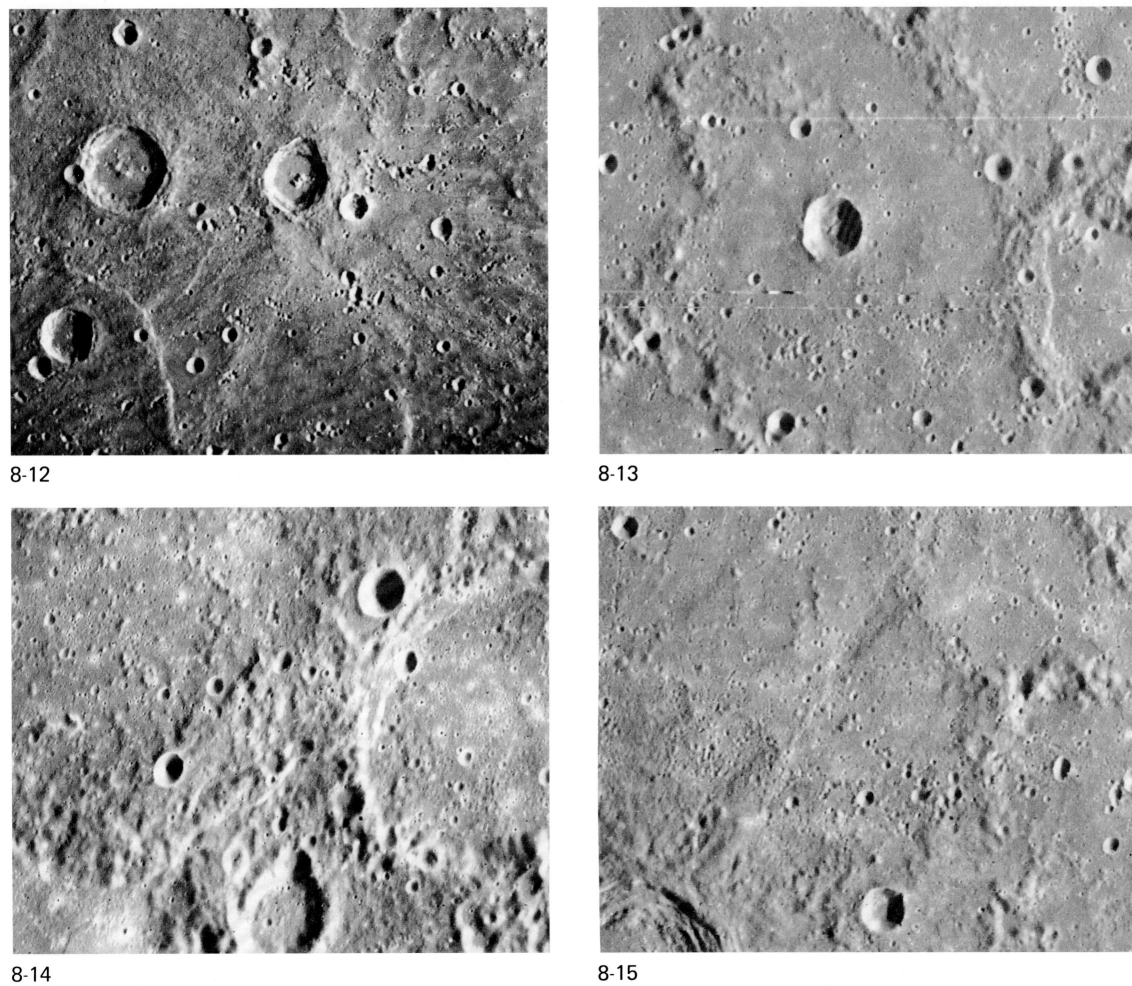

8-12

8-13

8-14

8-15

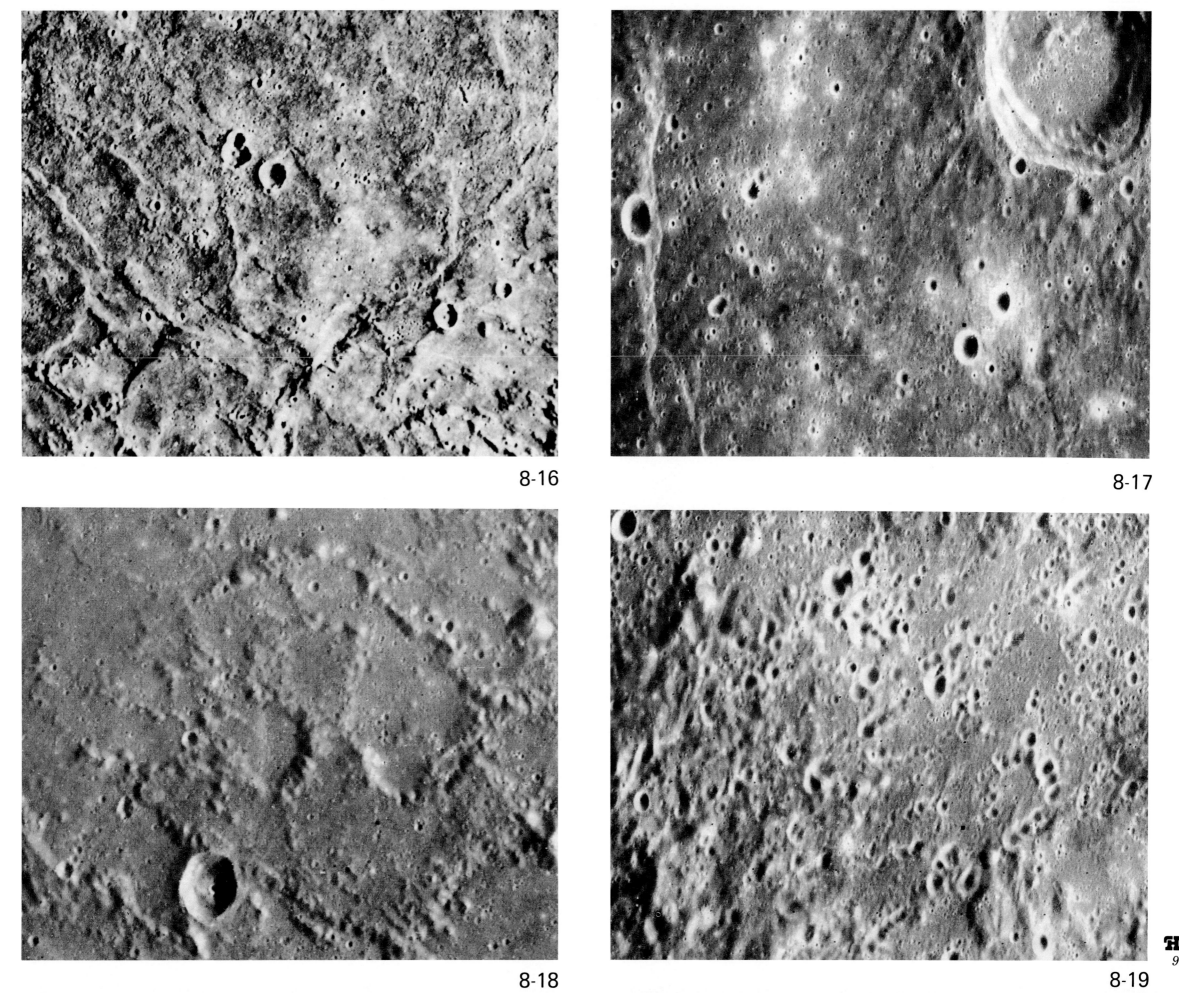

8-16

8-17

8-18

8-19

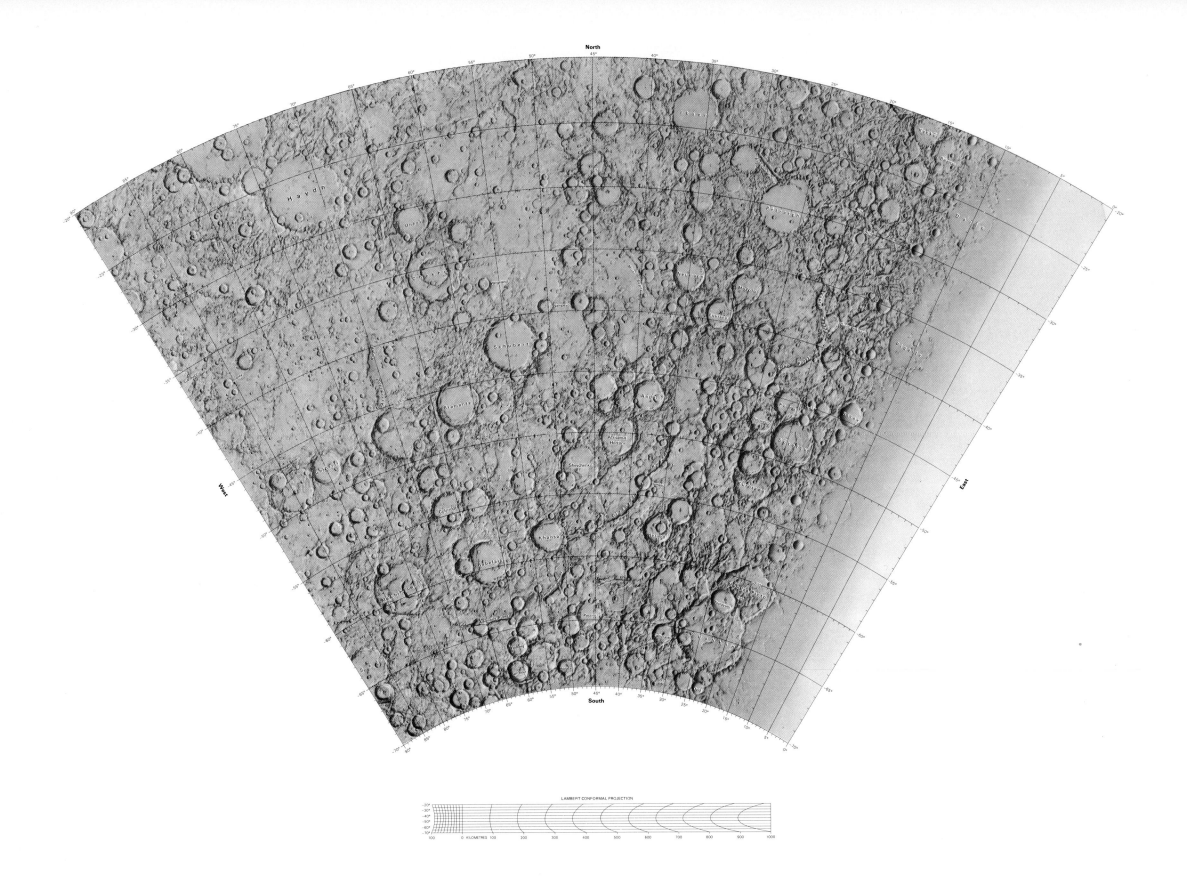

SHADED RELIEF MAP OF THE DISCOVERY QUADRANGLE OF MERCURY
(SOLITUDO HERMAE TRIS MEGISTI ALBEDO PROVINCE)
H-11
H 5M 45/45R
1976

H11

94

11-A COMPUTER PHOTOMOSAIC OF THE DISCOVERY QUADRANGLE OF MERCURY

H-11

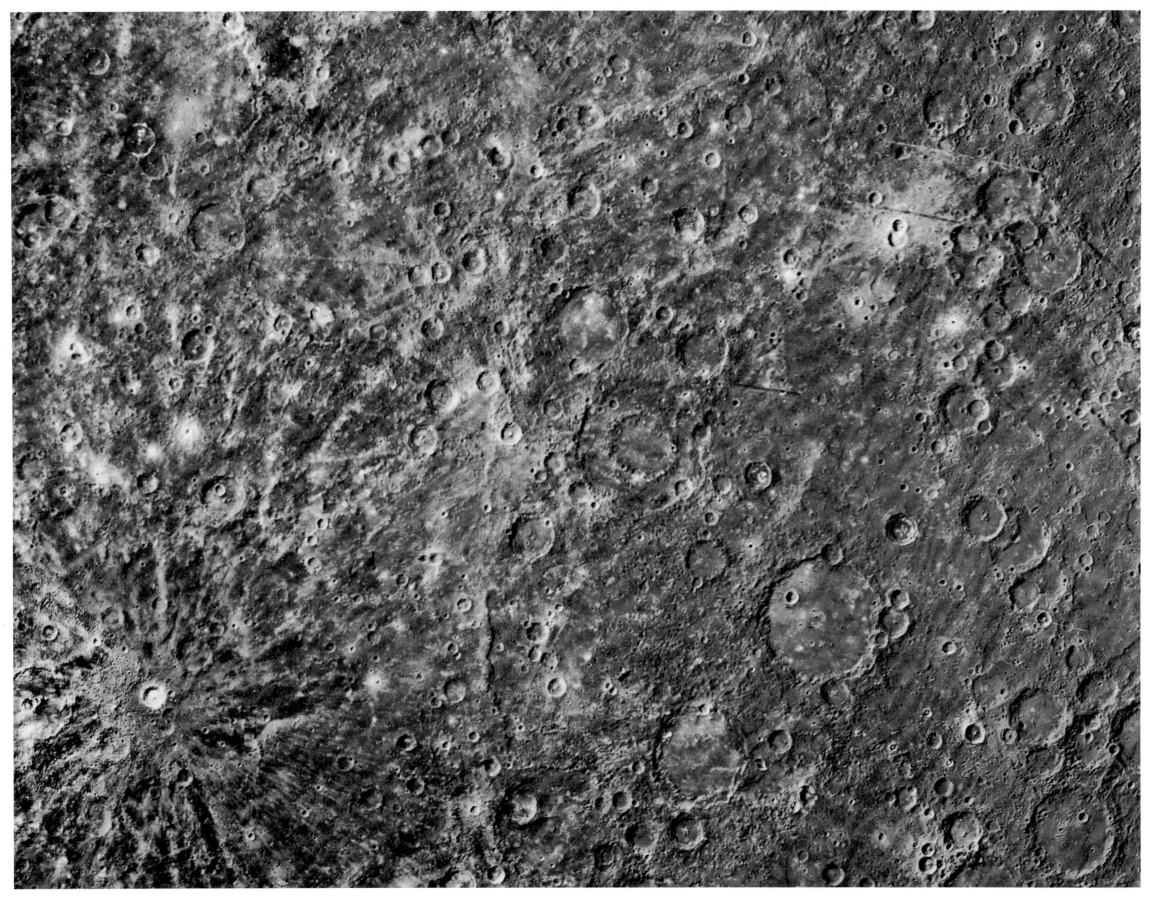

11-B   Enlarged view of the northwest region of the H-11 photomosaic

11-C   Enlarged view of the southwest region of the H-11 photomosaic

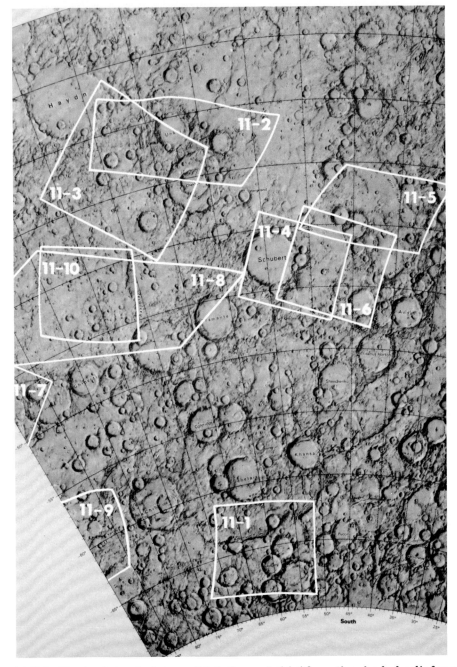

11-F1 Footprints of pictures 11-1 through 11-10 on the shaded relief map

11-2

11-3

11-4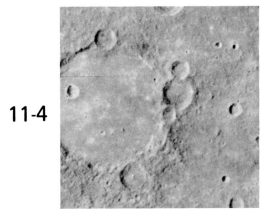

11-1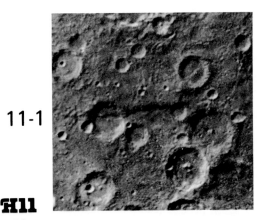

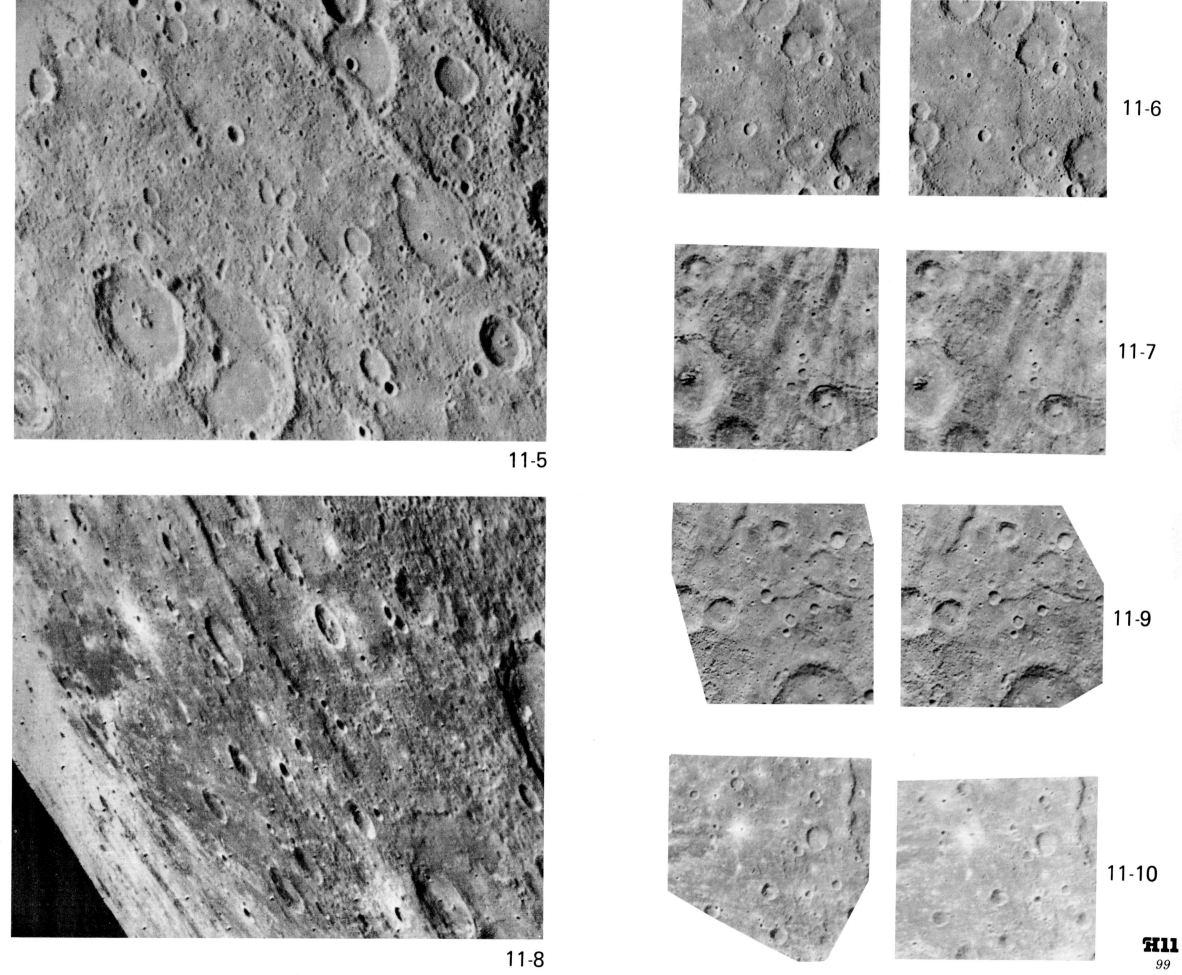

11-5

11-6

11-7

11-8

11-9

11-10

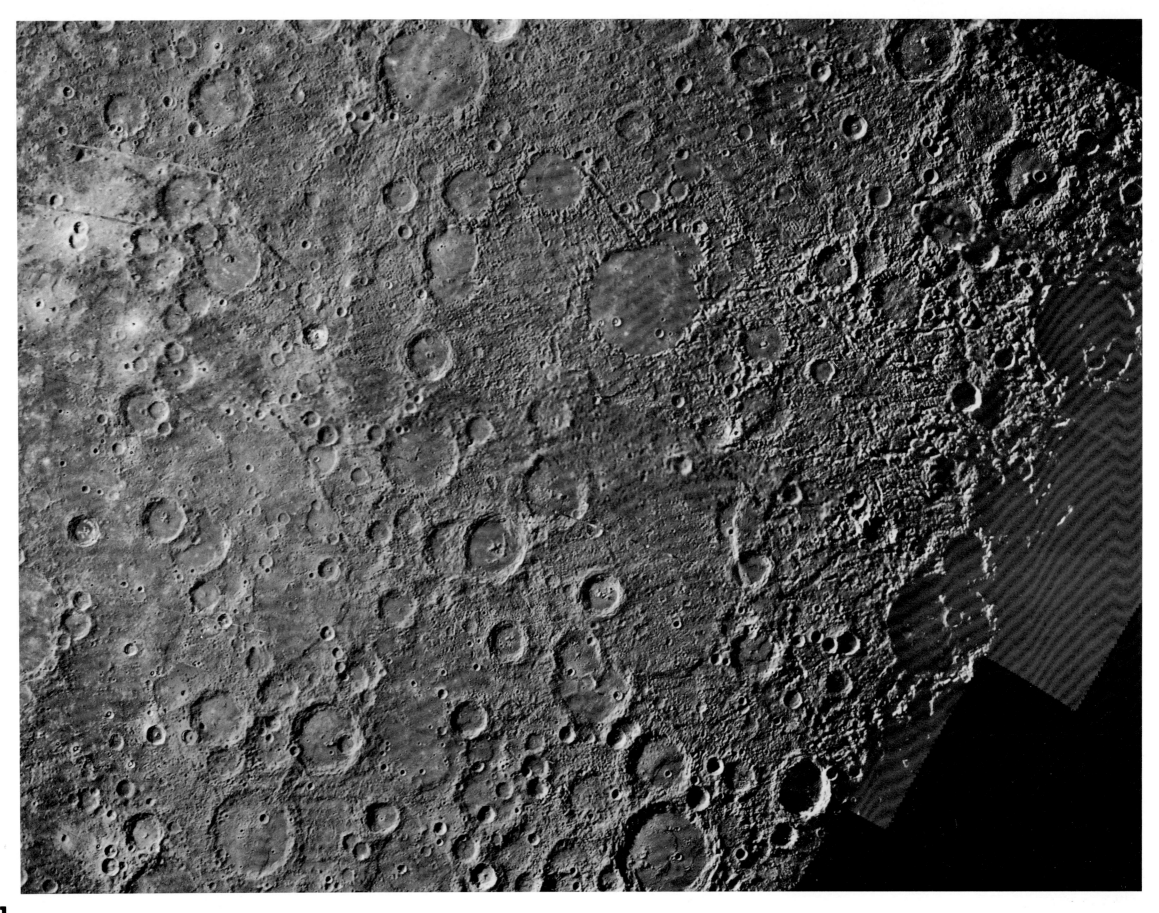

11-D   Enlarged view of the northeast region of the H-11 photomosaic

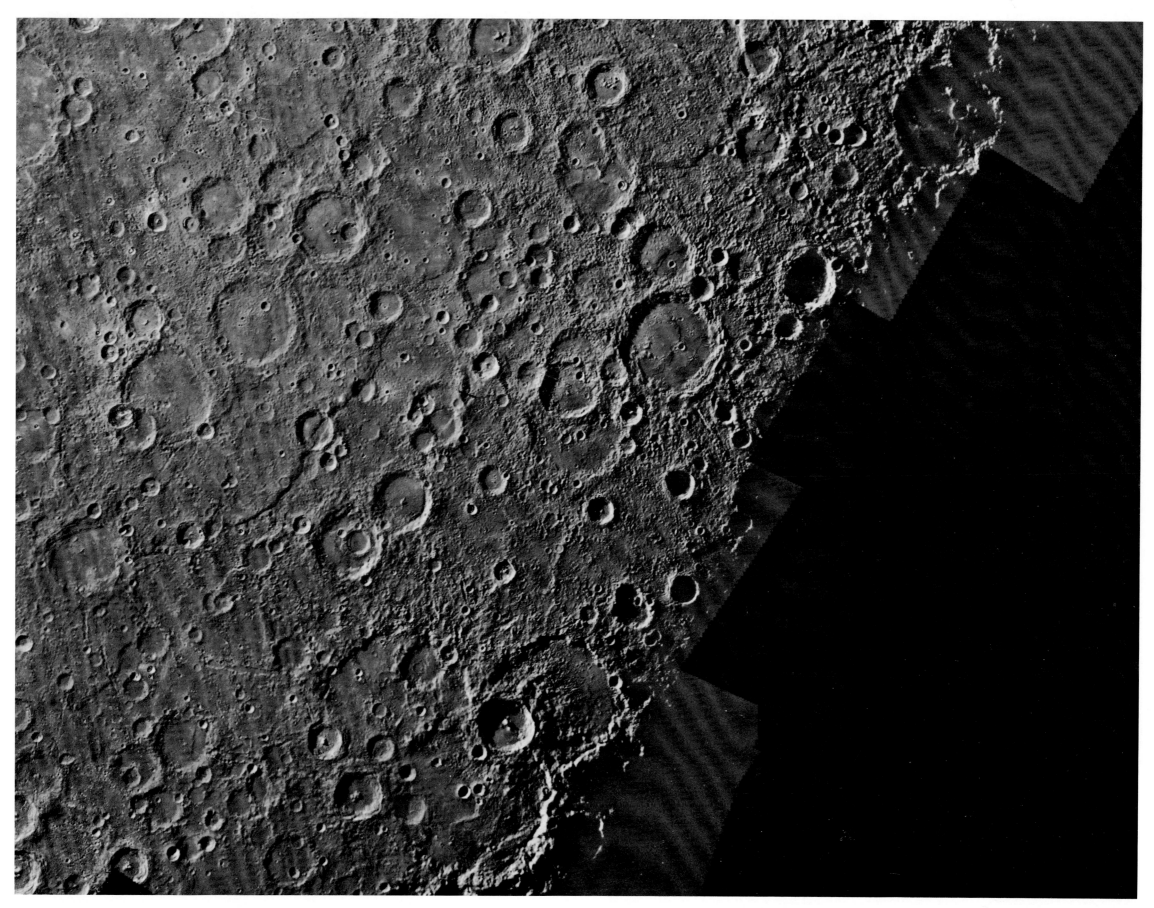

11-E   Enlarged view of the southeast region of the H-11 photomosaic

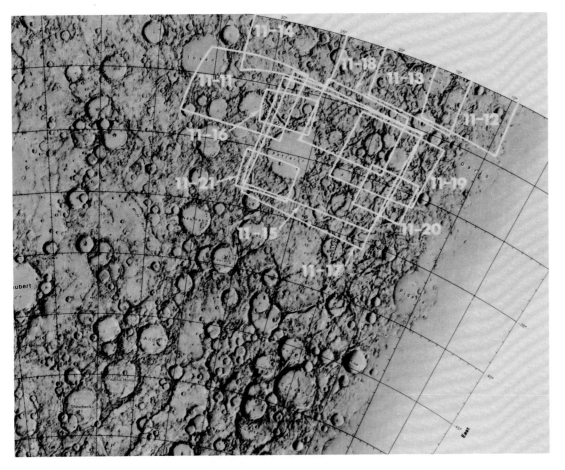

11-F2 Footprints of pictures 11-11 through 11-21 on the shaded relief map

11-11

11-12

11-13

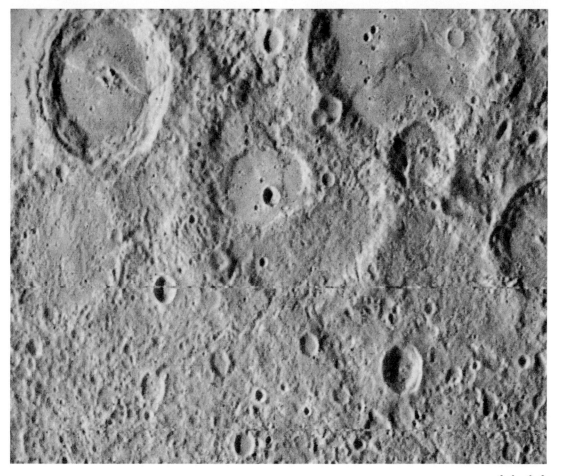

11-14

11-15

11-16

11-17

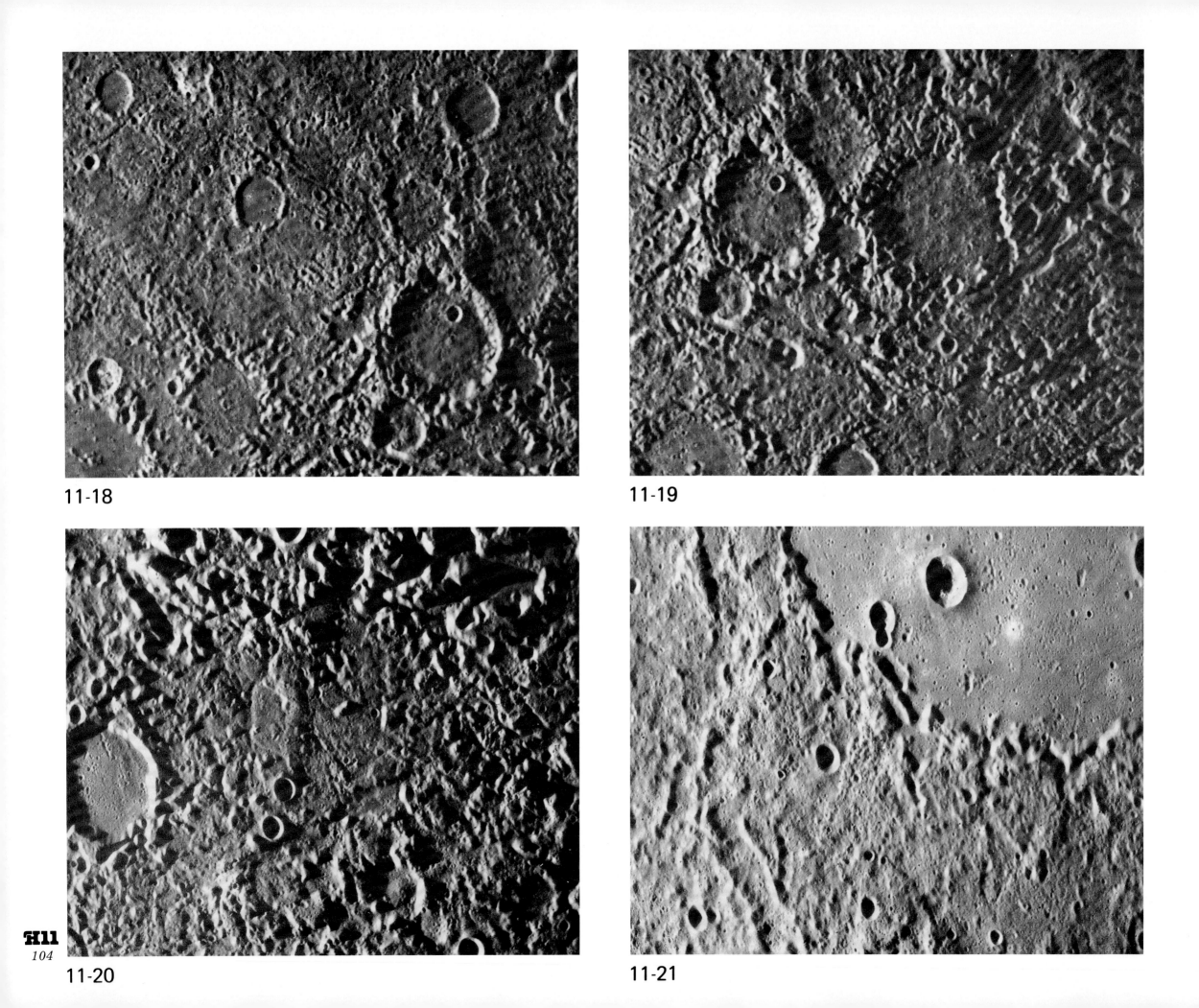

11-18

11-19

11-20

11-21

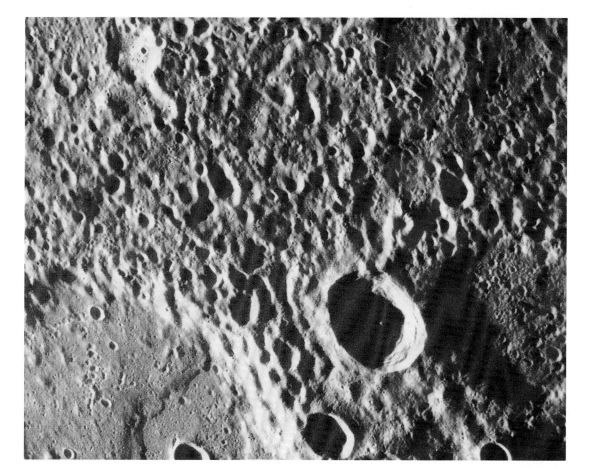

11-22

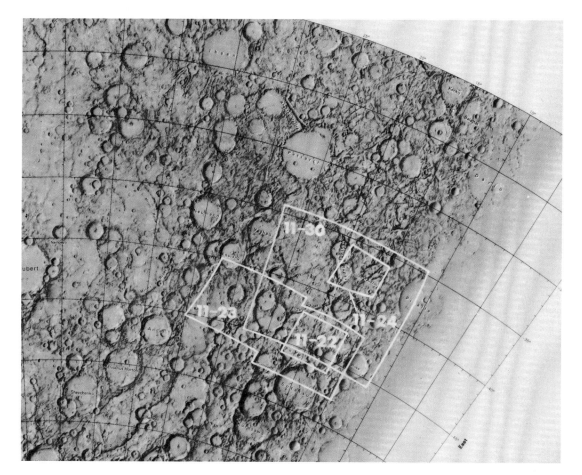

11-F3   Footprints of pictures 11-22, 11-23, 11-24, and 11-30 on the shaded relief map

11-23

11-24

11-25

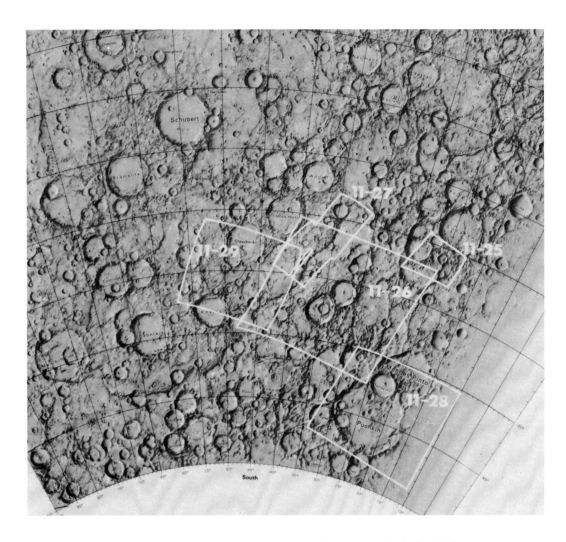

11-F4   Footprints of pictures 11-25 through 11-29 on the shaded relief map

11-26

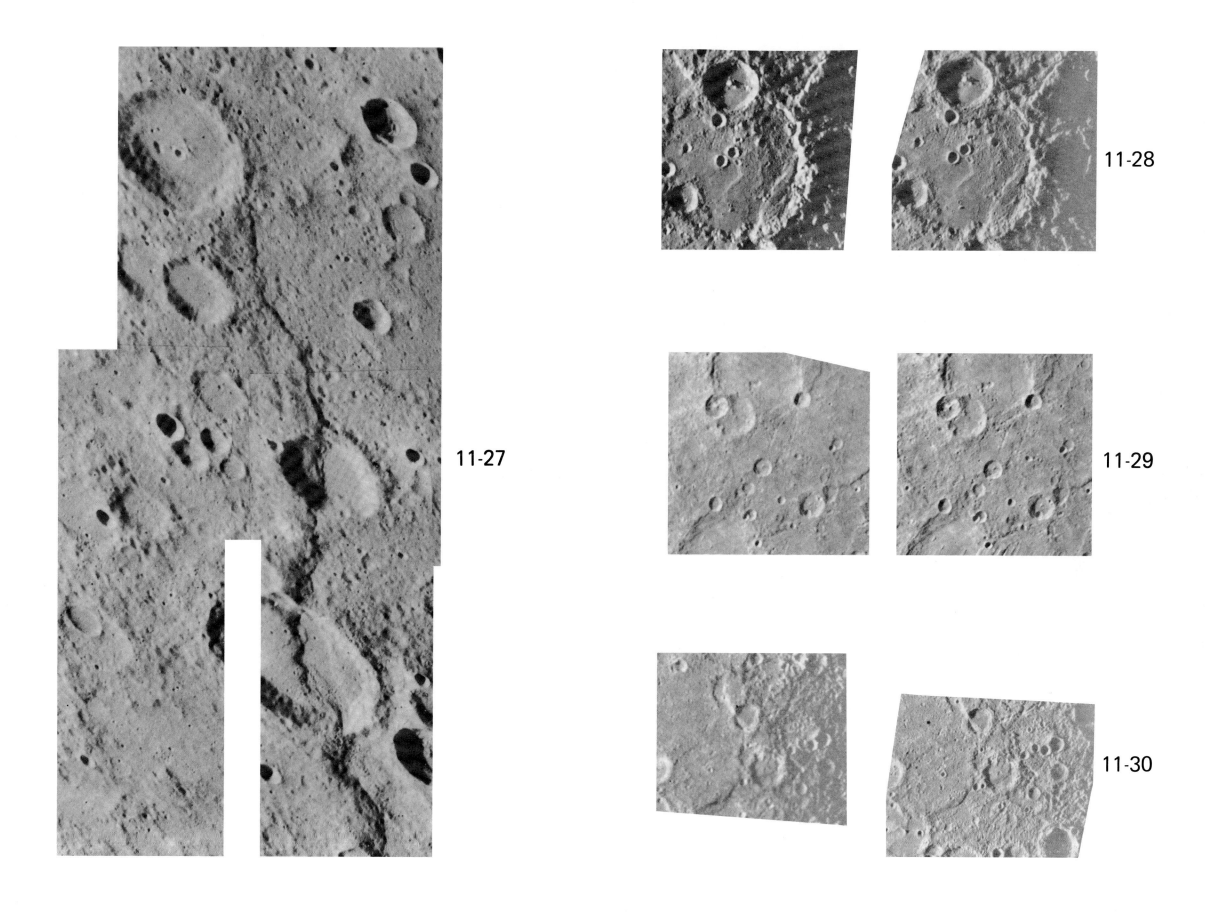

11-27

11-28

11-29

11-30

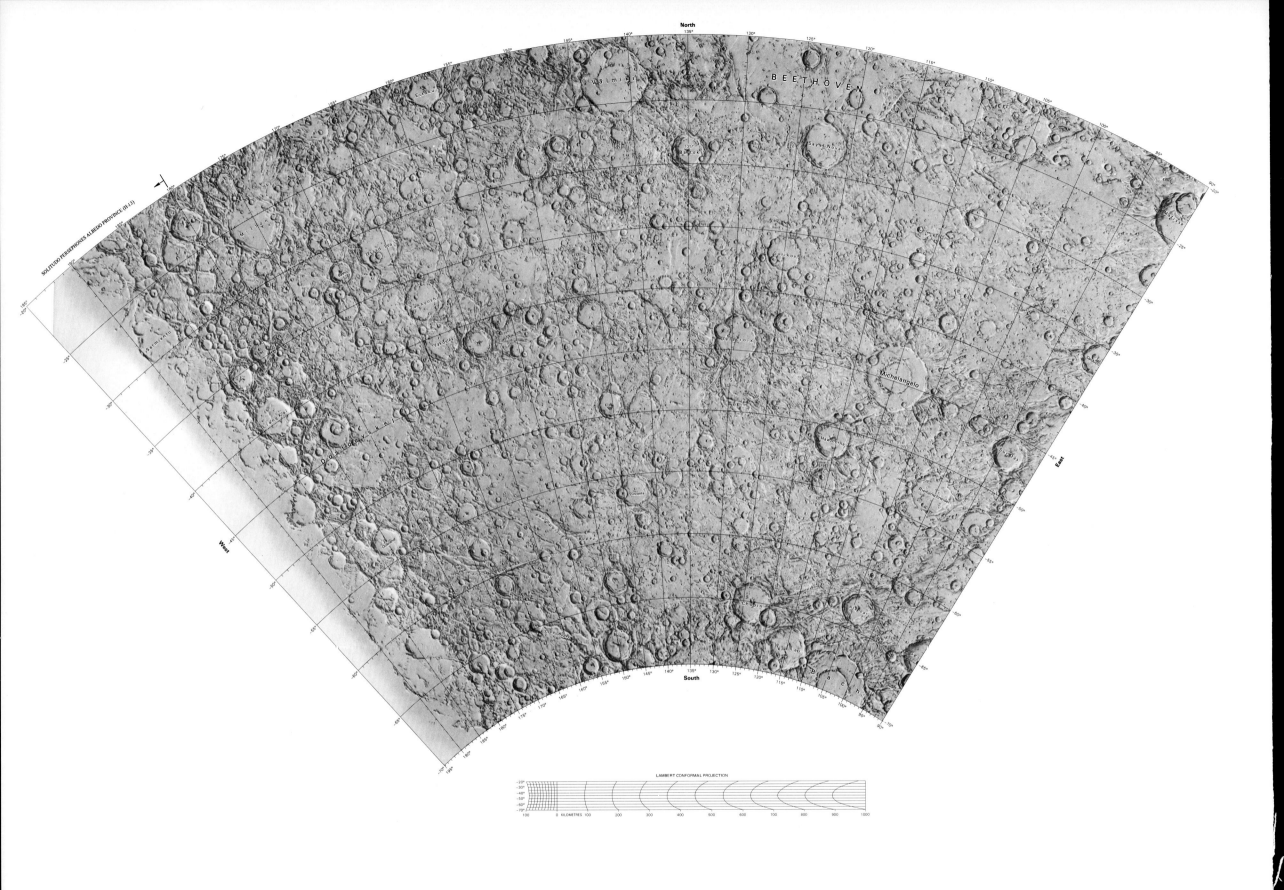

SHADED RELIEF MAP OF THE MICHELANGELO QUADRANGLE OF MERCURY

(SOLITUDO PROMENTHEI ALBEDO PROVINCE)

H-12

H 5M –45/135 R

1977

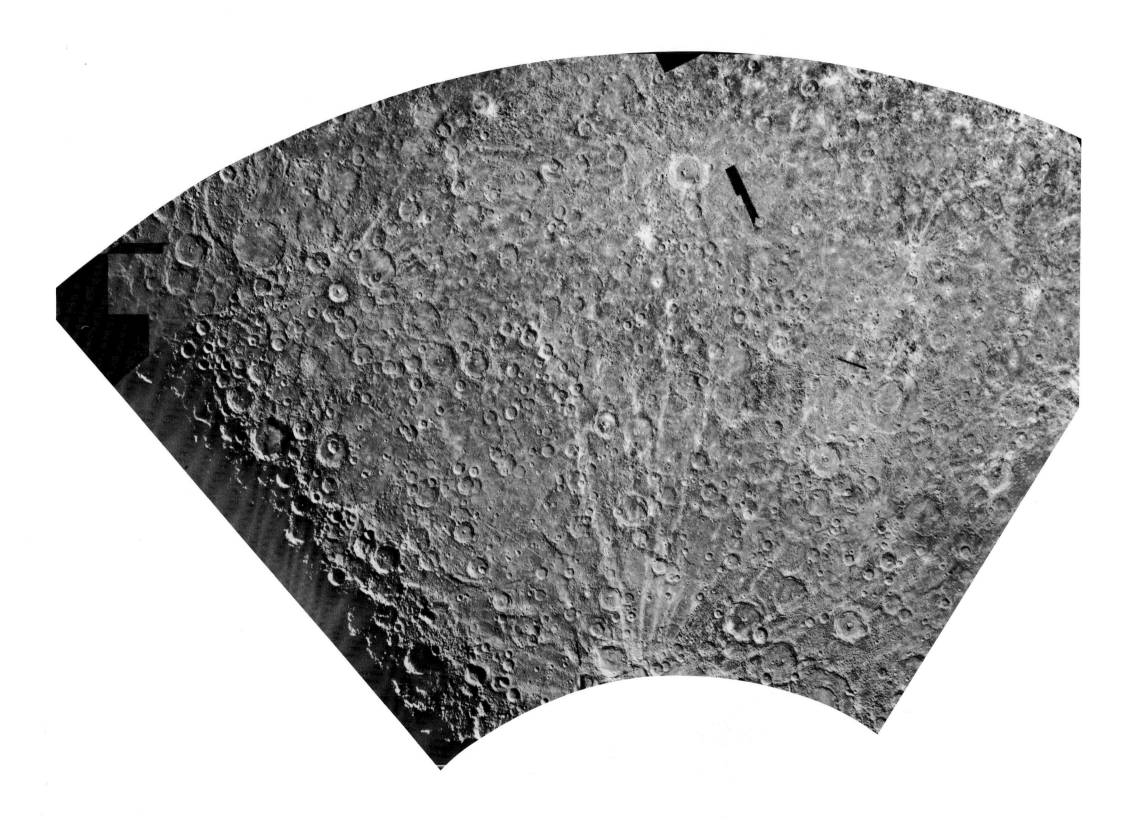

12-A   COMPUTER PHOTOMOSAIC OF THE MICHELANGELO QUADRANGLE OF MERCURY

H-12

12-B   Enlarged view of the northwest region of the H-12 photomosaic

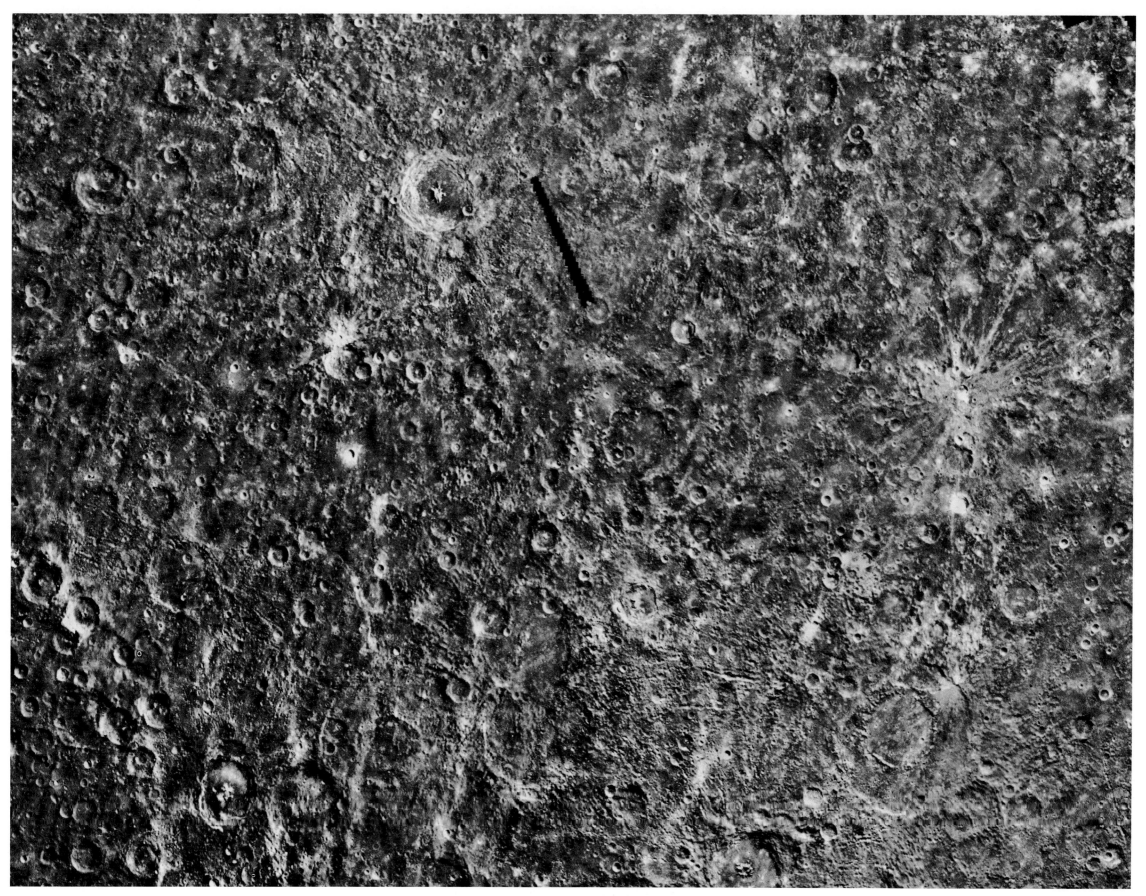

12-C   Enlarged view of the northeast region of the H-12 photomosaic

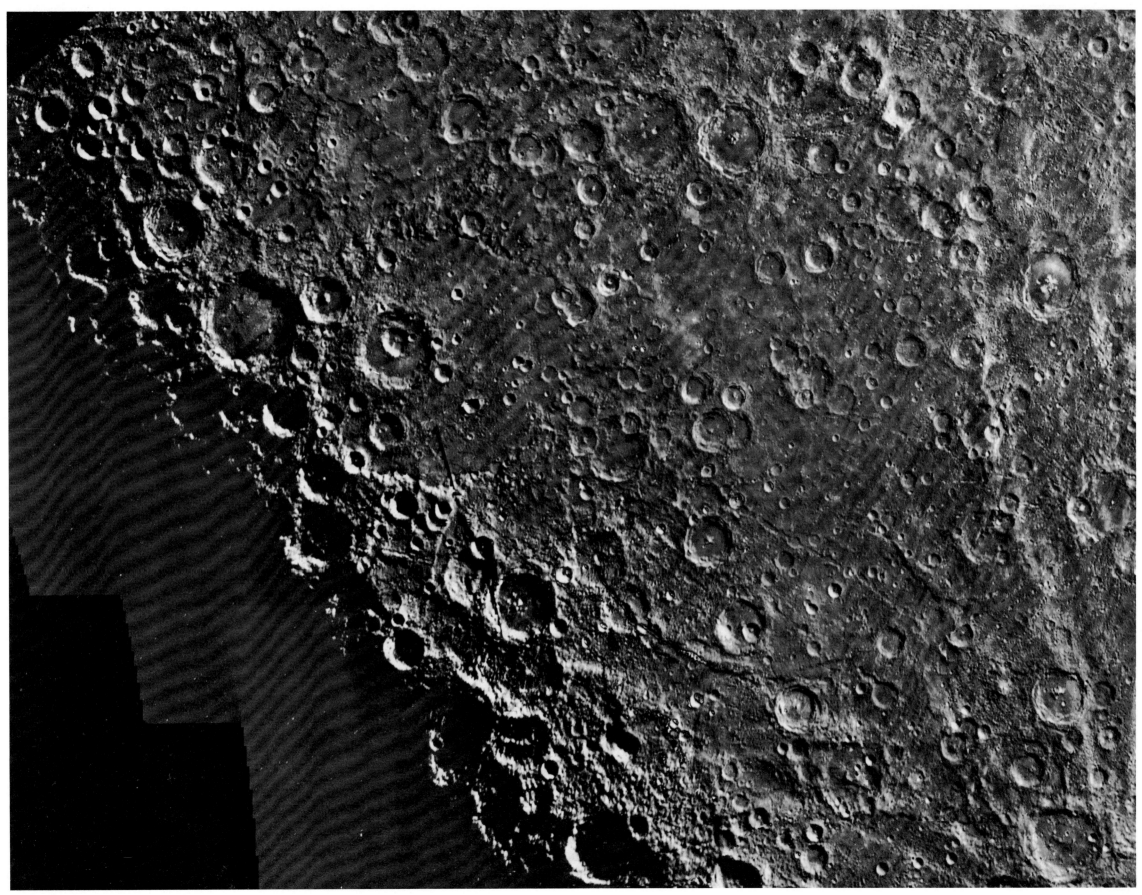

12-D   Enlarged view of the southwest region of the H-12 photomosaic

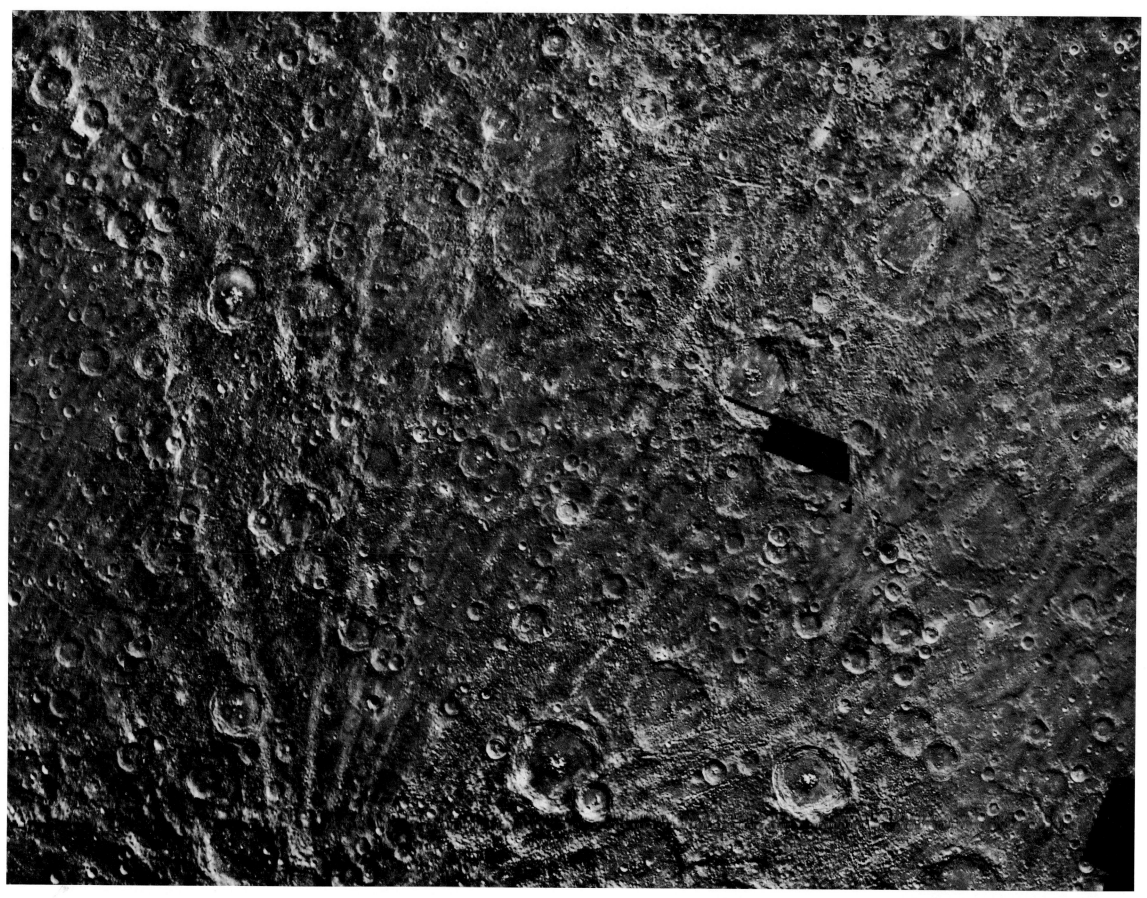

12-E   Enlarged view of the southeast region of the H-12 photomosaic

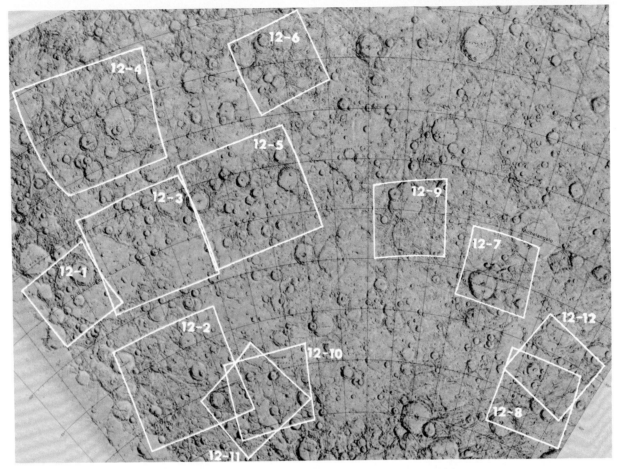

12-F1 Footprints of stereo pairs 12-1 through 12-12 on the shaded relief map

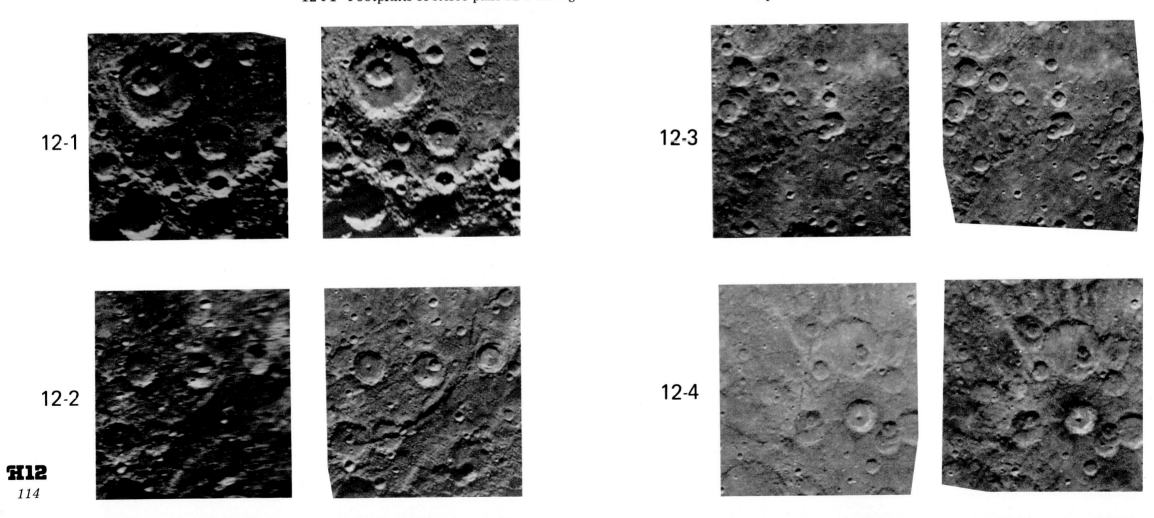

12-1

12-2

12-3

12-4

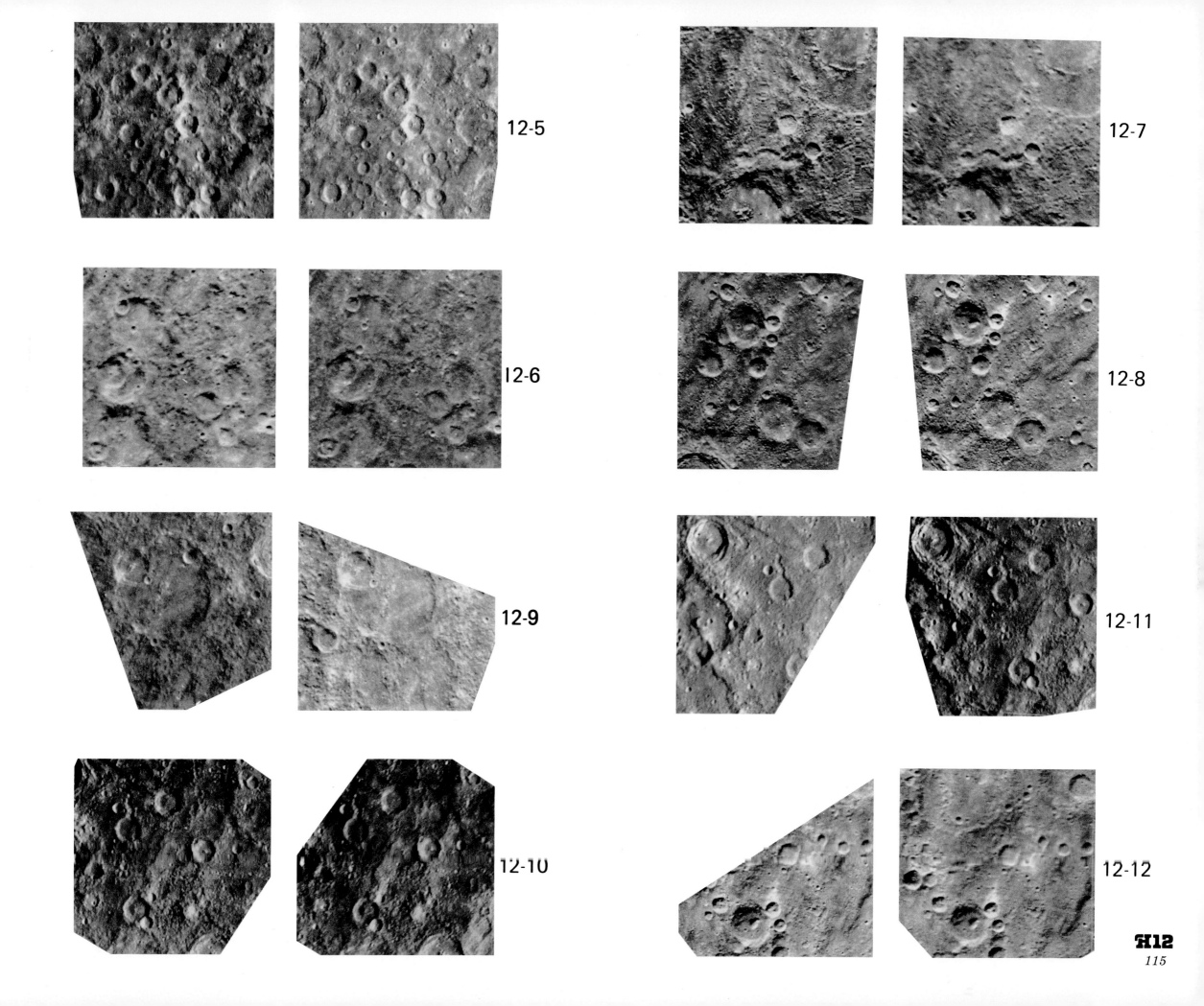

12-5

12-6

12-7

12-8

12-9

12-10

12-11

12-12

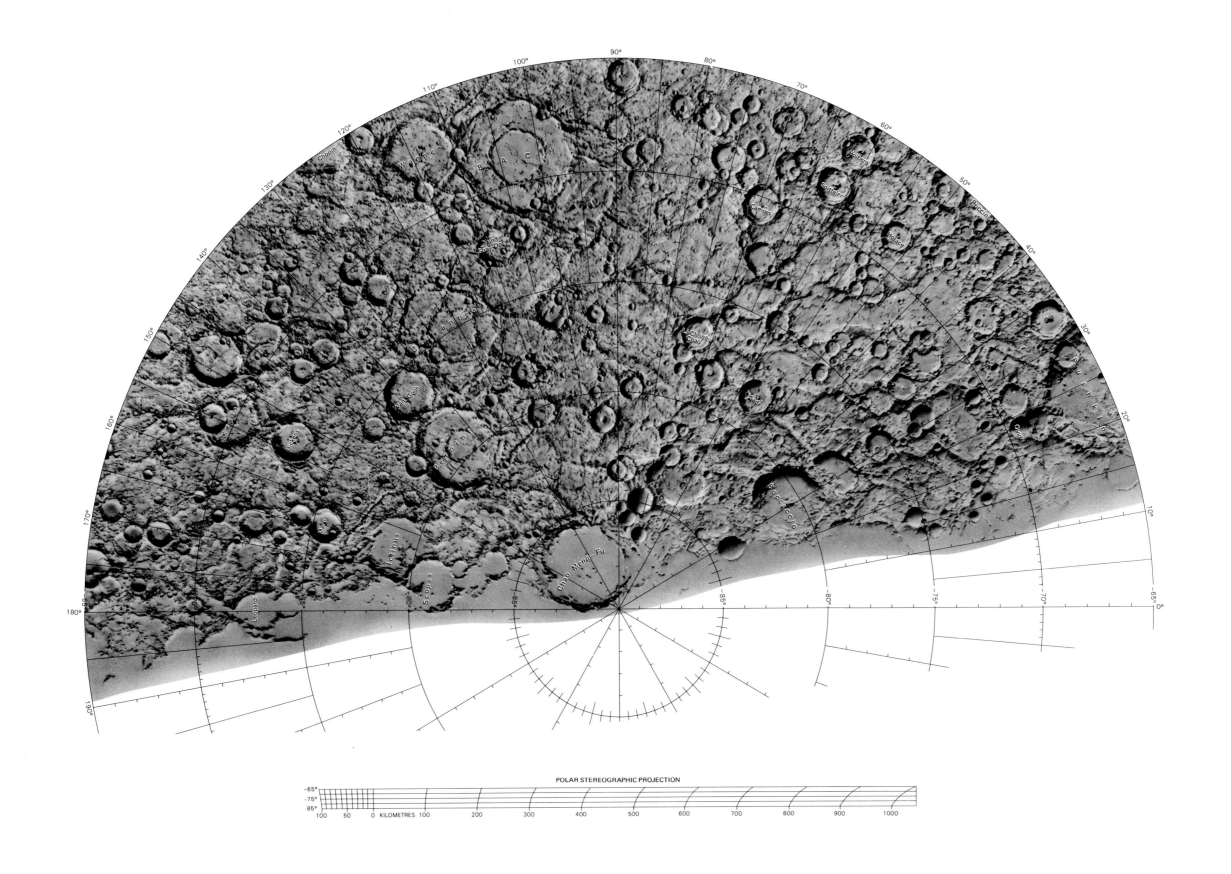

SHADED RELIEF MAP OF THE BACH AREA OF MERCURY

(AUSTRALIA ALBEDO PROVINCE)

H-15

H 5M –90/0 R

1976

POLAR STEREOGRAPHIC PROJECTION

15-A   COMPUTER PHOTOMOSAIC OF THE BACH AREA OF MERCURY

H-15

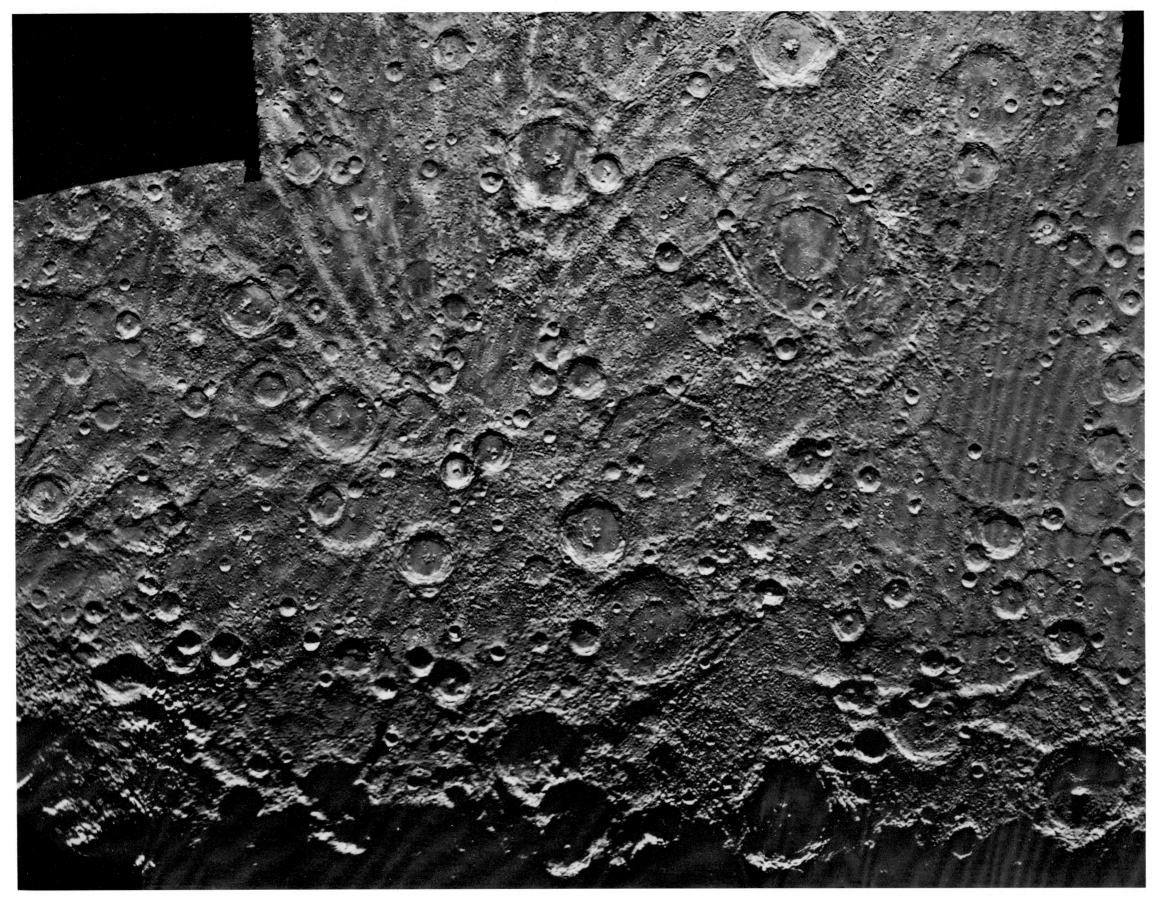

15-B   Enlarged view of the west region of the H-15 photomosaic

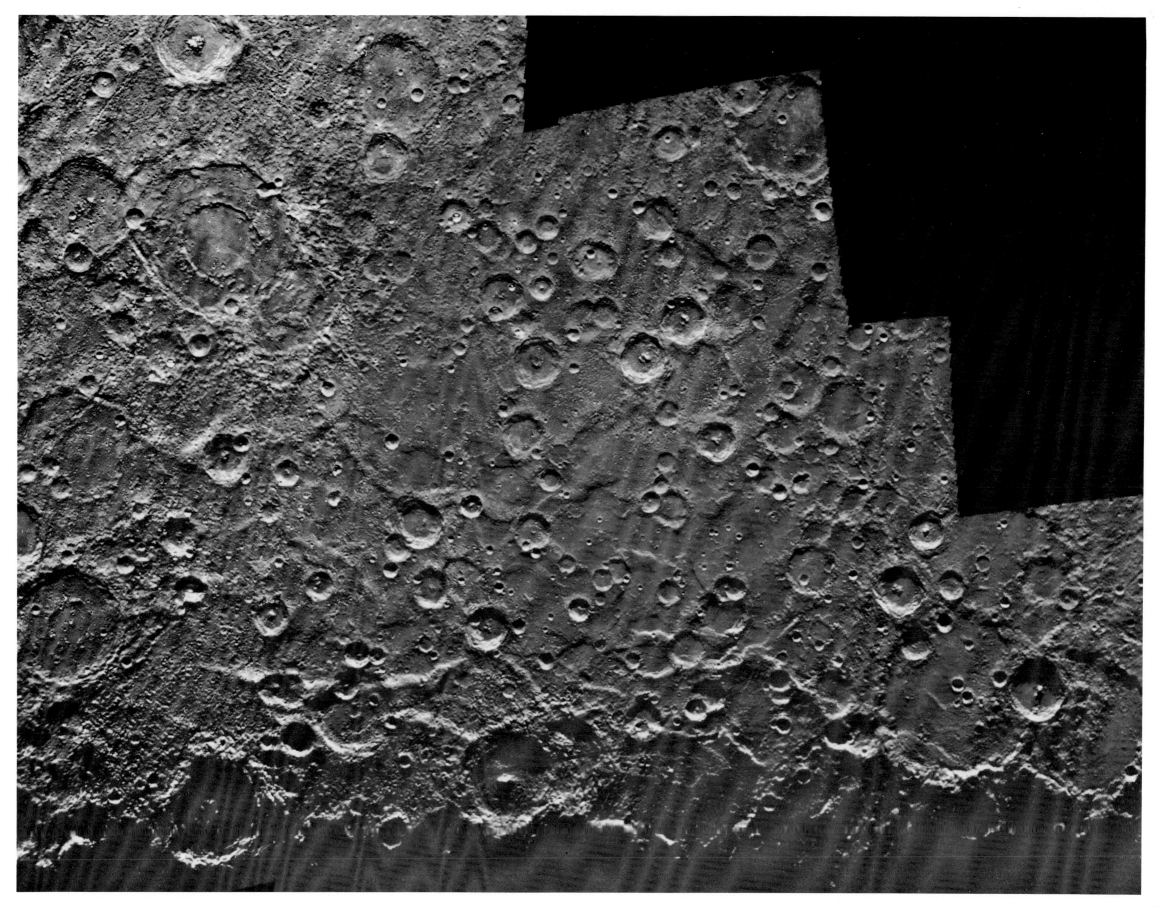

15-C   Enlarged view of the east region of the H-15 photomosaic

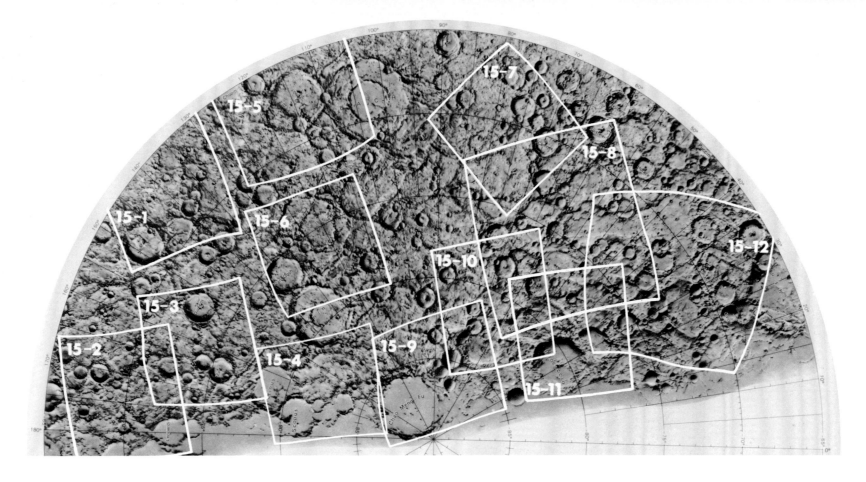

15-F1 Footprints of stereo pairs 15-1 through 15-12 on the shaded relief map

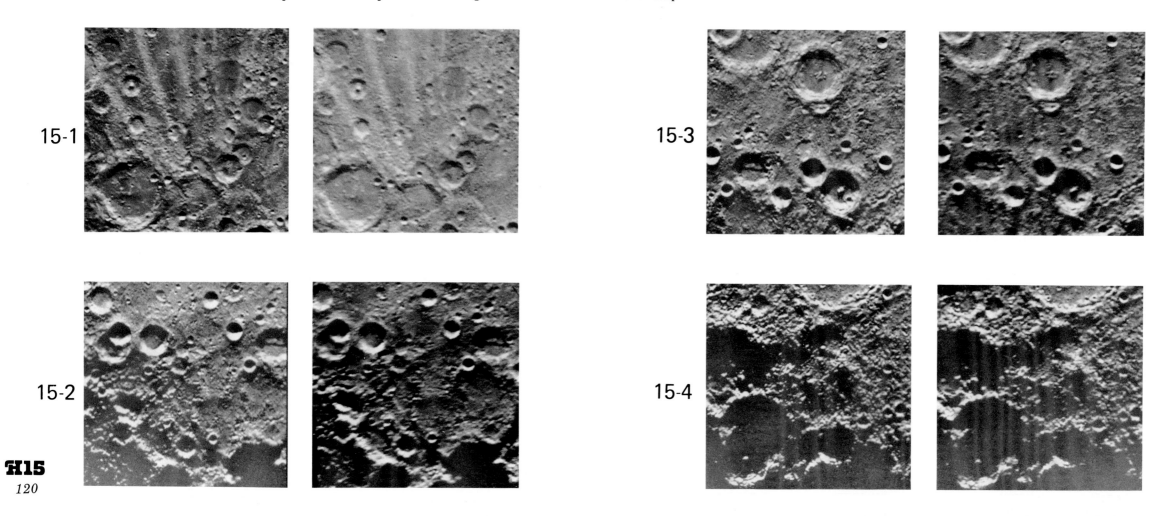

15-1

15-3

15-2

15-4

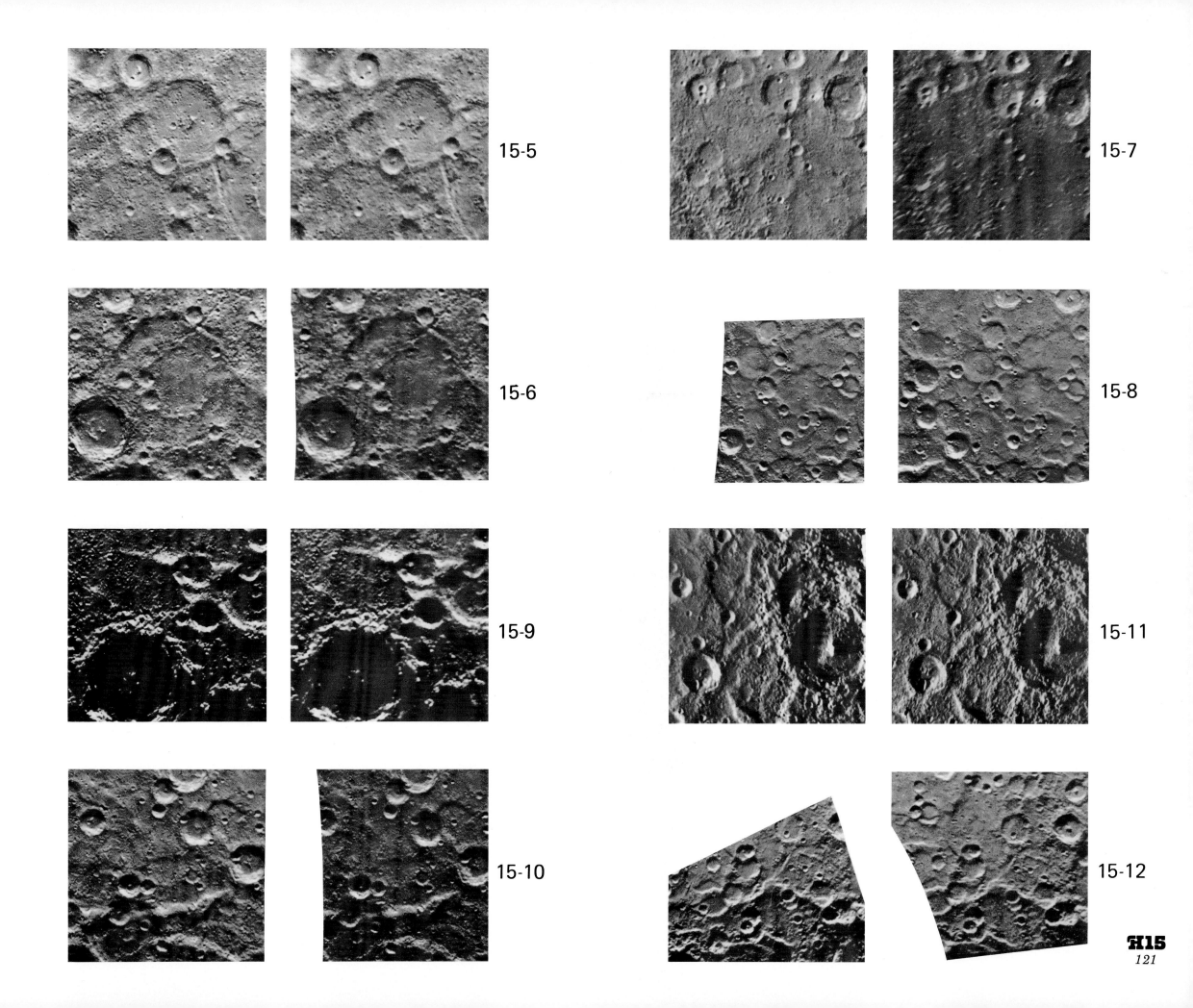

15-5

15-7

15-6

15-8

15-9

15-11

15-10

15-12

References

1. Antoniadi, E. M., *La Planète Mercure,* Gauthier-Villars, Paris, 1934. English translation by Patrick Moore, Keith Reid, Ltd., Shaldon, England, 1974.

2. Sandner, Werner, *The Planet Mercury,* The Macmillan Company, New York, 1963.

3. Klaasen, K. P., "Mercury Rotation Period Determined from Mariner 10 Photography,"*J. Geophys. Res.,* Vol. 80, No. 17, June 10, 1975, pp. 2415-2416.

4. Klaasen, K. P., "Mercury's Rotation Axis and Period," *Icarus,* Vol. 28, No. 4, August 1976, pp. 469-478.

5. Broadfoot, A. L., S. Kumar, M. J. S. Belton, and M. B. McElroy, "Mercury's Atmosphere from Mariner 10: Preliminary Results,"*Science,* Vol. 185, No. 4146, July 12, 1974, pp. 166-169.

6. Ness, N. F., K. W. Behannon, R. P. Lepping, and Y. C. Whang, "Magnetic Field of Mercury Confirmed," *Nature,* Vol. 255, 1975, pp. 204-206; see also N. F. Ness, K. W. Behannon, R. P. Lepping, and Y. C. Whang, "Observations of Mercury's Magnetic Field,"*Icarus,* Vol. 28, No. 4, August 1976, pp. 479-488.

7. Ogilvie, K. W., J. D. Scudder, R. E. Hartle, G. L. Siscoe, H. S. Bridge, A. J. Lazarus, J. R. Asbridge, S. J. Bame, and C. M. Yeates, "Observations at Mercury Encounter by the Plasma Science Experiment on Mariner 10," *Science,* Vol. 185, No. 4146, July 12, 1974, pp. 145-151; see also R. E. Hartle, K. W. Ogilvie, J. D. Scudder, H. S. Bridge, C. L. Siscoe, A. J. Lazarus, V. M. Vasyliunas, and C. M. Yeates, "Preliminary Interpretation of Plasma Electron Observations at the Third Encounter of Mariner 10 with Mercury,"*Nature,* Vol. 255, No. 5505, May 15, 1975, pp. 206-208.

8. Murray, B. C., R. G. Strom, N. J. Trask, and D. E. Gault, "Surface History of Mercury: Implications for Terrestrial Planets,"*J. Geophys. Res.,* Vol. 80, No. 17, June 10, 1975, pp. 2508-2514; see also B. C. Murray, M. J. S. Belton, G. E. Danielson, M. E. Davies, D. E. Gault, B. Hapke, B. O'Leary, R. G. Strom, V. Suomi, and N. Trask, "Mercury's Surface: Preliminary Description and Interpretation from Mariner 10 Pictures," *Science,* Vol. 185, No. 4146, July 12, 1974, pp. 169-179.

9. *The Planet Mercury,* National Aeronautics and Space Administration, Report SP-8085, March 1972.

10. Chase, S. C., E. D. Miner, D. Morrison, G. Munch, G. Neugebauer, and M. Schroeder, "Preliminary Infrared Radiometry of the Night Side of Mercury from Mariner 10,"*Science,* Vol. 185, No. 4146, July 12, 1974, pp. 142-145.

11. Zohar, S., and R. M. Goldstein, "Surface Features on Mercury,"*Astron. J.,* Vol. 79, No. 85, 1974, pp. 85-91.

12. Dunne, James A., "Mariner 10 Mercury Encounter," *Science,* Vol. 185, No. 4146, July 12, 1974, pp. 141-142.

13. Trask, N. J., and J. E. Guest, "Preliminary Geologic Terrain Map of Mercury,"*J. Geophys. Res.,* Vol. 80, No. 17, June 10, 1975, pp. 2461-2477.

14. Gault, D. E., J. E. Guest, J. B. Murray, D. Dzurisin, and M. C. Malin, "Some Comparisons of Impact Craters on Mercury and the Moon,"*J. Geophys. Res.,* Vol. 80, No. 17, June 10, 1975, pp. 2444-2460.

15. Trask, N. J., and R. G. Strom, "Additional Evidence of Mercurian Volcanism,"*Icarus,* Vol. 28, No. 4, August 1976, pp. 559-563.

16. Strom, R. G., N. J. Trask, and J. E. Guest, "Tectonism and Volcanism on Mercury,"*J. Geophys. Res.,* Vol. 80, No. 17, June 10, 1975, pp. 2478-2507.

17. Schultz, P. H., and D. E. Gault, "Seismic Effects from Major Basin Formations on the Moon and Mercury," *The Moon,* Vol. 12, February 1975, pp. 159-177.

18. Murray, B. C., "Mercury," *Scientific American,* Vol. 233, No. 3, September 1975, pp. 58-68.

19. Chapman, C. R., "Chronology of Terrestrial Planet Evolution: The Evidence from Mercury," *Icarus,* Vol. 28, No. 4, August 1976, pp. 523-536.

20. Guest, J. E., and D. E. Gault, "Crater Populations in the Early History of Mercury,"*Geophys. Res. Letters,* Vol. 3, No. 3, March 1976, pp. 121-123.

21. Wilhelms, D. E., "Mercurian Volcanism Questioned," *Icarus,* Vol. 28, No. 4, August 1976, pp. 551-558.

22. Richardus, P., and R. K. Adler, *Map Projections,* North-Holland Publishing Co., Amsterdam, 1972.

23. Lowell, Percival, *Memoirs of the American Academy of Sciences,* Vol. 12, 1897 (1902), p. 431; or *Popular Astronomy,* Vol. 4, 1896-7, Plate 32, p. 360.

24. Morrison, David, "IAU Nomenclature for Topographic Features on Mercury," *Icarus,* Vol. 28, No. 4, August 1976, pp. 605-606.

25. *Transactions of the International Astronomical Union,* Vol. 16B, D. Reidel Publishing Co., Dordrecht, 1977. Map prepared by A. Dollfus.

26. Rudaux, M. Lucien, "La Planète Mercure," *Bulletin de la société astronomique de France et revue mensuelle d'astronomie, de météorologie et de physique du globe,* Paris, 1928, p. 191.

27. *The Journal of the British Astronomical Association,* Vol. 46, No. 10, October 1936, Plate I: Planispheres of Mercury drawn by Jarry-Desloges in 1920, facing p. 357.

28. McEwen, H., "Mercury, Part III," *The Journal of the British Astronomical Association,* A.S.D. Maunder (ed.), Vol. 39, No. 8, London, 1928-1929, Plate 8, Figure 4, facing p. 311.

29. McEwen, H., "The Markings of Mercury," *The Journal of the British Astronomical Association,* Peter Doig (ed.), Vol. 36, Neill and Co., Ltd., Edinburgh, 1936, pp. 382-389.

30. Cruikshank, D. P., and C. R. Chapman, "Mercury's Rotation and Visual Observations," *Sky and Telescope,* Vol. 34, July 1967, p. 25.

31. Camichel, Henri, and Audouin Dollfus, "La Rotation et la cartographie de la planete Mercure," *Icarus,* Vol. 8, 1968, p. 221.

32. Murray, J. B., A. Dollfus, and B. Smith, "Cartography of the Surface Markings of Mercury," *Icarus,* Vol. 17, 1972, p. 581.

33. Davies, M. E., and R. M. Batson, "Surface Coordinates and Cartography of Mercury," *J. Geophys. Res.,* Vol. 80, No. 17, June 10, 1975, pp. 2417-2430.

34. Davies, M. E., and F. Y. Katayama, *The Control Net of Mercury: November 1976,* The Rand Corporation, R-2089-NASA, November 1976.

35. Danielson, G. E., Jr., K. P. Klaasen, and J. L. Anderson, "Acquisition and Description of Mariner 10 Television Science Data at Mercury," *J. Geophys. Res.,* Vol. 80, No. 17, June 1975, pp. 2357-2393.

36. Soha, J. M., D. J. Lynn, J. J. Lorre, J. A. Mosher, N. N. Thayer, D. A. Elliot, W. D. Benton, and R. E. Dewar, "IPL Processing of the Mariner 10 Images of Mercury," *J. Geophys. Res.,* Vol. 80, No. 17, June 10, 1975, pp. 2394-2414.

Craters	Quadrangle	Latitude (deg)	Longitude (deg)	Diameter (km)	Page
Abu Nuwas	H-6	17.5	21	115	58
Africanus Horton	H-11	-50.5	42	120	94
Ahmad Baba	H-3	58.5	127	115	40
Alencar	H-12	-63.5	104	85	108
Al-Hamadhani	H-2	39	89.5	170	32
Al-Jāhiz	H-6	1.5	22	95	58
Amru Al-Qays	H-8	13	176	50	82
Andal	H-11	-47	38.5	90	94
Aristoxenes	H-1	82	11	65	26
Asvaghosa	H-6	11	21	80	58
Bach	H-12, H-15	-69	103	225	108, 116
Balagtas	H-6, H-11	-22	14	100	58, 108
Balzac	H-8	11	145	65	82
Bartók	H-12	-29	135	80	108
Bashō	H-12	-32	170.5	70	108
Beethoven	H-7, H-12	-20	124	625	74, 108
Bello	H-7	-18.5	120.5	150	74
Bernini	H-15	-79.5	136	145	116
Boccaccio	H-15	-80.5	30	135	116
Boethius	H-7	-0.5	74	130	74
Botticelli	H-3	64	110	120	40
Brahms	H-3	58.5	177	75	40
Bramante	H-11	-46	62	130	94
Brontë	H-3	39	126.5	60	40
Brunelleschi	H-6	-8.5	22.5	140	58
Byron	H-6	-8	33	100	58
Callicrates	H-11	-65	32	65	94
Camões	H-15	-70.5	70	70	116
Carducci	H-11, H-12	-36	90	75	94, 108
Cervantes	H-15	-75	122	200	116
Chaikovskij	H-6	8	50.5	160	58
Chao Meng-Fu	H-15	-87.5	132	150	116
Chekov	H-11	-35.5	61.5	180	94
Chiang K'ui	H-7	14.5	103	40	74
Chŏng Ch'ŏl	H-3	47	116	120	40
Chopin	H-12, H-15	-64.5	124	100	108, 116
Chu Ta	H-7	2.5	106	100	74
Coleridge	H-11	-54.5	66.5	110	94
Copley	H-11	-37.5	85.5	30	94
Couperin	H-3	30	152	75	40
Dario	H-11	-26	10	160	94
Degas	H-3	37.5	127	45	40
Delacroix	H-12	-44.5	129.5	135	108
Derzhavin	H-2	44.5	35.5	145	32
Desprez	H-1	81	92	40	26
Dickens	H-15	-73	153	72	116
Donne	H-6	3	14	90	58
Dostoevskij	H-12, H-13	-44.5	177	390	108
Dowland	H-12, H-13	-53	180	80	108
Dürer	H-3, H-7	22	119.5	190	40, 74
Dvořák	H-6	-9.5	12.5	80	58
Eitoku	H-8, H-12	-21.5	157.5	105	82, 108
Equiano	H-11	-39	31	80	94
Futabatei	H-7	-15.5	83.5	55	74
Gauguin	H-1, H-3	66.5	97	75	26, 40
Ghiberti	H-11	-48	80	100	94
Giotto	H-6	12.5	56	150	58
Gluck	H-2	37.5	18.5	85	32
Goethe	H-1	79.5	44	340	26
Goya	H-8	-6.5	152.5	135	82
Guido d'Arezzo	H-11	-38	19	50	94
Handel	H-6	4	34	150	58
Harunobu	H-7	15.5	141	100	74
Hawthorne	H-12	-51	116	100	108
Haydn	H-11	-26.5	71.5	230	94
Heine	H-3	33	124.5	65	40
Hesiod	H-11	-58	35.5	90	94
Hiroshige	H-6	-13	27	140	58
Hitomaro	H-6	-16	16	105	58
Holbein	H-2	35.5	29	85	32
Holberg	H-11, H-15	-66.5	61	66	94, 116
Homer	H-6	-1	36.5	320	58
Horace	H-11, H-15	-68.5	52	48	94, 116
Hugo	H-2	39	47.5	190	32
Hun Kal		-0.5	20	1.5	64
Ibsen	H-6, H-11	-24	36	160	58, 94
Ictinus	H-15	-79	165	110	116
Imhotep	H-6	-17.5	37.5	160	58
Ives	H-12	-32.5	112	20	108
Jókai	H-1	72.5	136	85	26
Judah Ha-Levi	H-7	11.5	108	85	74
Kālidāsā	H-8	-17.5	180	110	82
Keats	H-12, H-15	-69.5	154	110	108, 116
Kenkō	H-6, H-11	-21	16.5	90	58, 94
Khansa	H-11	-58.5	52	100	94
Kuan Han-ch'ing	H-2	29	53	155	32
Kuiper	H-6	-11	31.5	60	58
Kurosawa	H-11	-52	23	180	94
Leopardi	H-15	-73	180	69	116
Lermontov	H-6	15.5	48.5	160	58
Liang K'ai	H-13	-39.5	183.5	105	108
Li Ch'ing-Chao	H-15	-77	73	60	116
Li Po	H-6	17.5	35	120	58
Lu Hsun	H-6	0.5	23.5	95	58
Lysippus	H-7	1.5	133	150	74
Ma Chih-Yuan	H-11	-59	77	170	94
Machaut	H-7	-1.5	83	105	74
Mahler	H-6	-19	19	100	58
Mansart	H-1	73.5	120	75	26
Mansur	H-3	47.5	163	75	40
March	H-3	31.5	176	55	40
Mark Twain	H-7	-10.5	138.5	140	74
Martí	H-15	-75.5	164	63	116
Martial	H-1	69	178	45	26
Matisse	H-7, H-12	-23.5	90	210	74, 108
Melville	H-2, H-6	22	9.5	145	32, 58
Mena	H-7	0.5	125	20	74
Mendes Pinto	H-11	-61	19	170	94
Michelangelo	H-12	-44.5	110	200	108
Mickiewicz	H-3, H-7	23.5	102.5	115	40, 74
Milton	H-8, H-12	-25.5	175	175	82, 108
Mistral	H-6	5	54	100	58
Mofolo	H-11	-37	29	90	94
Molière	H-6	16	17.5	140	58
Monet	H-2	44	9.5	250	32
Monteverdi	H-2	64	77	130	32
Mozart	H-8	8	190.5	225	82
Murasaki	H-6	-12	31	125	58
Mussorgskij	H-3	33	96.5	115	40
Myron	H-1	71	79.5	30	26
Nampeyo	H-11	-39.5	50.5	40	94
Nervo	H-3, H-4	43	179	50	40
Neumann	H-11	-36.5	35	100	94
Nizāmī	H-1	71.5	165	70	26
Ovid	H-11, H-15	-69.5	23	40	94, 116
Petrarch	H-11	-30	26.5	160	94
Phidias	H-8	9	150	155	82
Philoxenus	H-7	-8	112	95	74
Pigalle	H-11	-37	10.5	130	94
Po Chü-I	H-8	-6.5	165.5	60	82
Po Ya	H-11	-45.5	21	90	94
Polygnotus	H-6	0	68.5	130	58
Praxiteles	H-2	27	60	175	32
Proust	H-6	20	47	140	58
Puccini	H-11, H-15	-64.5	46	110	94, 116
Purcell	H-1	81	148	80	26
Pushkin	H-11, H-15	-65	24	200	94, 116
Rabelais	H-11	-59.5	62.5	130	94
Rajnis	H-7	5	96.5	85	74
Rameau	H-11	-54	38	50	94
Raphael	H-7	-19.5	76.5	350	74
Renoir	H-6	-18	52	220	58
Repin	H-6	-19	63	95	58
Riemenschneider	H-12	-52.5	100.5	120	108
Rilke	H-11	-44.5	13.5	70	94
Rodin	H-2, H-6	22	18.5	240	32, 58
Rubens	H-2	59.5	73.5	180	32
Rublev	H-8	-14.5	157.5	125	82
Rūdakī	H-6	-3.5	51.5	120	58
Sadī	H-15	-77.5	56	60	116
Saikaku	H-1	73	177	80	26
Sarmiento	H-13	-28.5	188.5	115	108
Sayat-Nova	H-12	-27.5	122.5	125	108
Scarlatti	H-3	40.5	99.5	135	40
Schoenberg	H-7	-15.5	136	30	74
Schubert	H-11	-42	54.5	160	94
Scopas	H-15	-81	173	95	116
Sei	H-11, H-12	-63.5	88.5	130	94, 108
Shakespeare	H-3	48.5	151	350	40
Shelley	H-12	-47.5	128.5	145	108

Craters	Quadrangle	Latitude (deg)	Longitude (deg)	Diameter (km)	Page
Shevchenko	H-11	-53	47	130	94
Sholem Aleichem	H-2	51	86.5	190	32
Sinan	H-6	16	30	140	58
Snorri	H-7	-8.5	83.5	20	74
Sophocles	H-8	-6.5	146.5	145	82
Sor Juana	H-2	49	24	80	32
Sōtatsu	H-11	-48	19.5	130	94
Spitteler	H-11, H-15	-68	62	66	94, 116
Stravinsky	H-2	50.5	73	170	32
Strindberg	H-3	54	136	165	40
Sullivan	H-7	-16	87	135	74
Sūr Dās	H-12	-46.5	94	100	108
Surikov	H-12	-37	125	105	108
Takayoshi	H-12	-37	164	105	108
Tansen	H-7	4.5	72	25	74
Thākur	H-6	-2.5	64	115	58
Theophanes	H-7	-4	143	50	74
Tintoretto	H-11	-47.5	24	60	94
Titian	H-6	-3	42.5	115	58
Tolstoj	H-8	-15	165	400	82
Ts'ai Wen-chi	H-2, H-6	23.5	22.5	120	32, 58
Ts'ao Chan	H-7	-13	142	110	74
Tsurayuki	H-11	-62	22.5	80	94
Tung Yüan	H-1	73.5	55	60	26
Turgenev	H-1, H-3	66	135	110	26, 40
Tyagaraja	H-8	4	149	100	82
Unkei	H-11	-31	62.5	110	94
Ustad Isa	H-12	-31.5	166	105	108
Vālmiki	H-7, H-12	-23.5	141.5	220	74, 108
Van Dijck	H-1	76.5	165	100	26
Van Eyck	H-3	43.5	159	235	40
Van Gogh	H-15	-76	135	95	116
Velázquez	H-2	37	54	120	32
Verdi	H-1, H-3	64.5	169	150	26, 40
Vincente	H-12	-56.5	143	85	108
Vivaldi	H-7	14.5	86	210	74
Vyāsa	H-2	48.5	80	275	32
Wagner	H-12, H-15	-67.5	114	135	108, 116
Wang Meng	H-7	9.5	104	170	74
Wergeland	H-11	-37	56.5	35	94
Wren	H-2	24.5	36	215	32
Yakovlev	H-12	-40.5	163.5	100	108
Yeats	H-6	9.5	35	90	58
Yun Sŏn-Do	H-15	-72.5	109	61	116
Zeami	H-8	-2.5	148	125	82
Zola	H-3	50.5	178	60	40

Mountains (Montes)	Quadrangle	Latitude (deg)	Longitude (deg)	Page
Caloris	H-3, H-4	22	180	40, 82
	H-8	40	180	

Plains (Planitiae)	Quadrangle	Latitude (deg)	Longitude (deg)	Page
Borealis	H-1	70	80	26
Budh	H-8	18	148	82
Caloris	H-4, H-8	30	195	40, 82
Odin	H-3, H-8	25	171	40, 82
Sobkou	H-3	40	130	40
Suisei	H-1, H-3	62	150	26, 40
Tir	H-8	3	177	82

Ridges (Dorsa)	Quadrangle	Latitude (deg)	Longitude (deg)	Page
Antoniadi	H-2, H-6	28	30	32, 58
Schiaparelli	H-8	24	164	82

Scarps (Rupes)	Quadrangle	Latitude (deg)	Longitude (deg)	Page
Adventure	H-11	-64	63	94
Astrolabe	H-11	-42	71	94
Discovery	H-11	-53	38	94
Endeavour	H-2	38	31	32
Fram	H-12	-58	94	108
Gjöa	H-12	-65	163	108
Heemskerck	H-3	25	125	40
Hero	H-12	-57	173	108
Mirni	H-11	-37	40	94
Pourquois-Pas	H-12	-58	156	108
Resolution	H-11	-62	52	94
Santa Maria	H-6	6	20	58
Victoria	H-2	50	32	32
Vostok	H-11	-38	19	94
Zarya	H-11	-42	22	94
Zeehaen	H-3	50	158	40

Valleys (Valles)	Quadrangle	Latitude (deg)	Longitude (deg)	Page
Arecibo	H-11	-27	29	94
Goldstone	H-6	-15	32	58
Haystack	H-6	5	46.5	58
Simeiz	H-6	-12.5	65	58

Acknowledgments

We would like to express our thanks and appreciation to Raymond M. Batson, Chief Cartographer of the Mercury series of maps, and to airbrush artists Jay L. Inge, Patricia M. Bridges, and Susan L. Davis, all of the U.S. Geological Survey (Branch of Astrogeological Studies) at Flagstaff, Arizona, for their help and patience in adapting their maps to the Atlas format. Inge was responsible for the H-1, H-6, and H-15 maps, Bridges for the H-3, H-7, H-8, and H-12 maps and Davis for the H-2 and H-11 maps.

We are grateful to the many people at the National Aeronautics and Space Administration, Jet Propulsion Laboratory, and Boeing Aircraft Company who made the Mariner 10 mission a success. We recognize that the project was in existence for many years and that the "team" consisted of hundreds of people who contributed to the design, manufacture, and testing of the spacecraft, to mission operations, and to mission management. We would like to mention a few of the people we worked with during this phase of our lives. At NASA Headquarters, N. William Cunningham efficiently managed the program. Also contributing were Arnold C. Belcher, Maurice E. Binkley, Stephen C. Hiett, Henry E. Holt, James C. Hood, Diane M. Mangel, Nicholas W. Panagakos, Guenter K. Strobel, Margaret S. Ware, and Althea R. Washington.

At the Jet Propulsion Laboratory, we valued our association with W. Eugene Giberson, the project manager, his deputies John R. Casani and Victor C. Clarke, Jr., and project scientist James A. Dunne, and appreciate their dedication to the project. We worked with many outstanding people at JPL on the project and would like to mention a few: Dallas F. Beauchamp, Wailen E. Bennett, Frank E. Bristow, Frank Colella, Virgil B. Combs, Vincent L. Evanchuk, Richard M. Goldstein, William B. Green, Mark Herring, A. Adrian Hooke, Ralph A. Johansen, Jeremy B. Jones, Kenneth P. Klaasen, Lawrence K. Koga, Susan K. La Voie, Gerald S. Levy, Donald J. Lynn, Robert J. MacMillin, David D. Norris, Donna Shirley Pivirotto, William I. Purdy, Jr., Michael J. Sander, James M. Soha, Anthony J. Spear, Ronald C. Spriestersbach, Gael F. Squibb, Norma J. Stetzel, David L. Thiessen, Robert I. Toombs, Fred E. Vescelus, Peter B. Whitehead, and Steven J. Zawacki.

From the Boeing Aircraft Corporation we appreciated the efforts of James M. Ellis, James J. Farrell, Merlyn J. Flakus, Charles W. Luke, and Rod A. Zieger.

We are indebted to James A. Dunne, JPL, John F. McCauley, USGS, and Ermine van der Wyk, JPL, for valuable and timely review of draft manuscripts.

Finally we would like to recognize Bruce C. Murray for his energetic and dedicated leadership of the television team and his encouragement in the preparation of this Atlas.

To order copies of the photographs and mosaics in this Atlas, send the picture number (left column below) to the National Space Science Data Center, Code 601, Goddard Space Flight Center, National Aeronautics and Space Administration, Greenbelt, Maryland 20771.

The shaded relief maps are reproductions of the U.S. Geological Survey 1:5,000,000 series; they may be ordered by I number from Branch of Distribution, U.S. Geological Survey, 1200 So. Eads Street, Arlington, Virginia 22202 or Box 25286, Federal Center, Denver, Colorado 80225. The I number may be found from the H number appearing on the map, as follows:

Index

☆ U.S. GOVERNMENT PRINTING OFFICE : 1978 O—247-681